Some nice things people
have said abo

G000123258

Often we do not even spot the subtle tra
or spouse to becoming a carer. The A
reference for all who care for others, or th _____ to do so in the future.

Elizabeth Mills OBE
Hon Director – Homeshare International

It gives me great pleasure to endorse this very timely book which ticks so many boxes, it is hard to believe that someone hasn't come up with the idea before. Its particular appeal is that it is written from life-long care experiences of a very special woman, Carer Min, backed up with clinical, social and policy research on our ageing populations. The principal difference here is that these personal recollections and bold facts are presented in a sensitive, humorous and non-patronising way without losing the sense of urgency attached to the need to wake up to the reality of what it means to get old and be old. Most importantly, it provides comprehensive practical and emotional guidance for those of us who have ageing parents and friends by offering both sound advice on how to cope with tricky situations and links to resources to back up the wise words. I hope that the book will be read by anyone involved with older people including their relatives, friends, volunteers and health and social work professionals. It will certainly be on my bookshelf and not gathering dust.

Kate Davidson PhD
Co-Director – Centre for Research on Ageing and Gender,
University of Surrey, UK

Action for Ageing gives the reader simple and practical advice on how to look after their ageing loved ones to help prevent accidents and illness. Everyone should read it, put it into action and help keep their family and friends safe and in good health. Chris and Robin should be very proud of their work. I am sure it will help many families.

Gary Lumby MBE
Director of Small Business Banking,
Clydesdale and Yorkshire Banks

The Action for Ageing book is a well researched resource and as an information guide I would highly recommend it as leading the way to assist carers, those that they are providing the care to and any support services that are involved in assisting them in this process.

Delia Naylor
Sales Director – Access Independent
Specialist Provider of Occupational Therapy Services, UK

ACTION FOR AGEING

Chris Minett
Robin Minett

ACTION FOR AGEING

Published:
Vicheko Limited, London
for www.ActionForAgeing.com

LONDON

All Rights Reserved © Vicheko Limited

First published in 2011

Interior design and layout by David Vernon www.gravington.co.uk
Cover design by Mark Bailey www.EXPdesign.co.uk

Printed and bound by Lightning Source UK Ltd

The right of Chris Minett and Robin Minett to be identified as authors of this work has been asserted in accordance with Section 77 of the Copyright, Designs and Patent Act 1988.

ISBN   978-0-9568220-4-8

This book and the intention behind it
is dedicated to

Sandy Bursnall

and

Peter Minett

Carer Min

The Vase and Two Glasses of Wine

If you are ever feeling like life is too busy and there aren't enough hours in the day, a great story I once heard was about a vase and two glasses of wine.

A philosophy lecturer stood in front of his class with some objects on his lectern.

After his students sat down, he held up a large glass vase and filled it with snooker balls, one by one.

When he was done, he asked his class if the vase was full.

The class said "Yes".

The lecture held up a large handful of marbles and fed them into the vase.

The marbles fell in and around the snooker balls.

When he was done, the lecturer asked if the vase was full.

The class said "Yes".

Next, the lecturer held up a piled handful of crushed ice and fed that into the vase.

With a shake, the crushed ice fell between the marbles and the balls.

The lecturer then asked if the vase was full.

The whole class roared "YES!"

The lecturer then opened a bottle of wine and filled two glasses.

He then poured the wine from the glasses into the vase.

The class cheered loudly.

After the cheering stopped, the lecturer looked up at them and said, "What you need to appreciate is that your life is like this vase. The snooker balls are like the big, important parts of your life – your partner, your family, your kids, friends, passions and your health. The stuff that matters.

The marbles... they are the aspects of your life like your home, your car and your job.

The crushed ice is all the rest. The trivial stuff. By putting the crushed ice in your vase first, you won't be able to fit in all your marbles and snooker balls.

That's the same as your life.

If all of your effort and focus is on the trivial stuff, then there is little time left over for the important things.

Recognise what things are vital for your wellbeing.

Make time for your partner.

Make time for your kids, your parents and grandparents.

Have your health checked regularly.

Book a table at your partner's favourite restaurant.

Stay in bed for an extra five minutes or play another round of cards for winner-take-all.

The lawn mowing can wait and the dirty dishes in the sink won't go anywhere.

Stay focused on the snooker balls in the vase – the big stuff.

Have a sense of what your priorities are.

Don't stress about the crushed ice and marbles. That's the little stuff.

The crushed ice especially, might seem significant now but in a short time will have melted away to nothing and be quickly forgotten.

A student then asked what the two glasses of wine were for.

The lecturer laughed and said "Good question."

The wine in the vase is to remind you that regardless of how busy you are and how full life seems, you can always squeeze in a glass (or two) of wine with a friend.

Disclaimer

This book has been prepared by Vicheko Limited and contains general information only which we hope will be of use to you. Nothing in this book should be construed as the giving of specific advice and it should not be relied on as a basis for any decision or action. Vicheko Limited does not accept any liability arising from its use. We aim to ensure the information is as up to date and accurate as possible, but please be aware that certain areas and practices are subject to change from time to time.

All names of people and places have been changed to protect confidentiality and privacy.

Please note that the inclusion of named agencies, companies, products, services or publications in this book does not constitute a recommendation or endorsement by Vicheko Limited.

Please also note that this book has been produced for entertainiment purposes only. The views and actions described are those only of the authors and are not to be taken as advice or recommendations for action. The laws and codes of best practise pertaining care provision in the country of the reader are always to be understood, respected and followed.

Foreword

Getting older now is no longer what it used to be 50 or even 20 years ago. Along with rising life expectancy, more and more older citizens feel they still have a lot to give and to experience even after they have reached an advanced age.

Although this should be regarded and celebrated as a major scientific and social achievement, a lot has to be done at all levels to enable everyone to enjoy life at all ages and make the best of one's potential for the benefit of all.

The Madrid International Plan of Action on Ageing, adopted in April 2002, and the European Year 2012 for Active Ageing and Solidarity between Generations are examples of the UN and EU commitment to promoting active and healthy ageing at a global level. The pilot European Innovation Partnership on Active and Healthy Ageing, adopted by the European Council in February 2011, is also an important step towards a better coordination of national policies on ageing and pooling of resources at EU level.

These actions aim at impacting on older citizens' overall wellbeing and their life within their community and AGE Platform Europe hopes they will provide the impetus for an ongoing and increasing promotion of an age-friendly society for many years to come.

However, close relatives and friends remain the main sources of support in old age and providing accurate information on how to assist our older loved ones in everyday life is crucial.

This is why this Action for Ageing book can make a valuable contribution towards improving older people's quality of life and help build up the supportive environment they need to enjoy a healthy and active life in old age.

Small details can make a big difference and it is essential to join action at all levels to achieve positive and effective results on the ground and make ageing not only a natural process, but also a worthwhile, safer and fulfilling time of life.

Anne-Sophie Parent
Secretary General
AGE Platform Europe

AGE Platform Europe is a European network of organisations of and for people who are 50+, which aims to provide a voice and promote the interests of senior citizens across Europe. AGE has seven main policy areas: Anti-discrimination, Employment and Active Ageing, Social Inclusion, Social Protection, Health, Accessibility and Solidarity between Generations. **www.age-platform.eu**

For information on UK membership and activities of AGE Platform Europe, please contact the AGE Platform Europe UK secretariat via email **international@ageuk.org.uk**

Preface

The idea for this book was conceived during a family holiday in Spain in the summer of 2010.

After years of listening to his mother, Robin (Carer Min), share her countless observations and tips about caring for older people and lovingly-told anecdotes about various relatives and clients, her eldest son Mike made a suggestion. Mike challenged his mother to capture all of her valuable advice, knowledge and stories and craft them into a book so that others may enjoy and learn from them.

Thus, the seed of the idea was planted.

By six the following morning, Carer Min sat at a wobbly table in the garden, with a strong cup of tea and began writing down her tips and stories. Fifty years of providing care as a loving daughter, niece, cousin, wife and professional carer was then poured into 28,000 handwritten words.

At the same time Robin's youngest son, Chris, started extensive research into the world of ageing and the care of older people. He was amazed at the huge and various challenges that the ageing population faced, coupled with the desperate and immediate need for a profound and seismic change in the general public's attitude towards ageing.

The big realisation was that people of all ages, across society and around the world needed to stop and think about what the ageing of a loved one actually means. How it will impact their life and the lives of their loved ones. The wonderful opportunities and potential challenges of later life. How the sooner people start to take action to try and prevent injuries from happening, the better off everyone will be, physically, emotionally, socially and financially. It is in all our interests to help older people live as safely, healthily and happily as possible.

Here, the traditional 'parentcraft' book is turned on its head, to help people prepare for caring and the life changing situations of our ageing loved ones in a non-prescriptive and sensitive way. For many people it is uncharted territory – much like being a new parent or child carer.

Following the research for the book and the apparent need to help raise people's awareness of what opportunities and challenges ageing can represent and the simple steps that can help improve later life wellbeing, Chris and his family have launched the social enterprise Action for Ageing.

So one year after that family holiday, the enterprise has been launched and the book is now published.

Action for Ageing
297 tips to improve the
safety, health and wellbeing
of your ageing loved ones

Acknowledgements

We would like to thank our family and friends for their support, encouragement, ideas, feedback, patience and enthusiasm.

We would like to give special thanks to Mike (brother/son) whose original idea and committed input has made this book and ActionForAgeing what they are and what they may be.

Sam and Rufus, Mylie, Estelle, Priscilla, Gerald and Dorothy Minett, along with Kevin, Chase and Katie Bursnall and Brad, Kim and Misha Jackson, have all played a role in helping make this book what it is and are part of its fabric and the good that we hope may come from it. Your rock solid support has enabled this book to evolve from an idea over the dinner table into something real. This will hopefully be of benefit to many people, in many ways, for a long time.

We would also like to thank David Vernon of gravington.co.uk for his tireless work in putting the book together under extremely tight timelines. Mark Bailey and Rob Ellis at EXPdesign.co.uk for their fantastic design work. Freelance editor Kate Thomas (kate1thomas@gmail.com) for her editing. Clive Goddard at www.goddardcartoons.co.uk for the wonderful illustrations.

Thanks to Delia Naylor and her occupational therapy colleagues at AccessIndependent.co.uk, Nicola Robinson from Age UK, Irene Kingston, Anne Mélard from AGE Platform Europe, Lions Club International (for allowing inclusion of the Message in a Bottle program), Caroline Moye at Independent Age, Hannah Clack and Heather Bowker with Alzheimer's Society, Andrew Haigh, Karl Elliott and the Engage Mutual team, Jess Sweetman and the PR team of The Royal National Institute of Blind People (RNIB), Chris Walsh and Wise Owls, Rebecca Griffin and Cara Fullelove at Action for Hearing Loss (formerly the RNID – Royal

National Institute for Deaf People), and Elizabeth Mills OBE with Homeshare International for your invaluable feedback, permissions, suggestions and most importantly encouragement.

An extra-special thank you also to Dr Kate Davidson, whose wonderful suggestions and enthusiastic support has been very much appreciated.

Robin (Carer Min) would especially like to acknowledge the hundreds of older people she has visited in their homes and spent time with over many years. During these visits many dramas occurred. Inevitably, these wonderful people would meet these challenges with great dignity and humour and held confidence that their carer would solve the issue. This, Robin hopes she did. Most of the time…

If one person's later life has been made safer, healthier or happier because of actions taken from this book, then all of the hard work in putting it together has been worthwhile.

May today and every day be a special one for you and your family.

Best regards,

Robin and Chris

September 2011

Contents

References for statistics and prices:

Please note that there are a number of statistics, facts and figures in this book. For people who wish to know the source of the information, a full reference and links to the source are available in the 'Statistics' section of our Resources page: **www.ActionForAgeing.com/Resources**

Once in the Statistics section, you will be able to search for the statistic, price or fact by page number and/or Topic.

Introduction

"Hello?"

"It's about your mum. She's had a fall."

This phone call is how people in their thirties, forties and fifties, people in the middle of a busy afternoon at work, find out that their life and that of their loved ones, has possibly just changed in a massive way, forever.

Welcome to the world of Caring.

Ageing? Who?

It's likely you'll cheerfully acknowledge that your parents, partner, family and friends are all ageing.

You might even (less cheerfully) admit the same goes for you too.

Yes, we're ALL ageing.

What we generally don't like to acknowledge very well is that our parents, partner, friends, family or ourselves, are not only ageing, but also becoming MORE VULNERABLE too.

Bizarrely though, whilst our ageing loved ones may be the most precious people in our life, we may not have seriously considered whether their age has started to have an impact on their health or safety in their home and in their life.

Have you actually ever stopped and seriously thought about how ageing of your loved ones currently is or will soon be making an impact on their life and wellbeing and that of you and your family?

This is a **big**, important and **unavoidable** question.

A question you may one day need to answer.

More directly, have you asked yourself these questions?

- Who will look after _____ when they can no longer look after themselves at home, or if they injure themselves by falling over in the bath and become immobile for three months, six months or for life?
- What care options are available? In what ways can family and friends help?
- Who will pay for their medical bills, home carer or nursing home?
- Will they come and live with me?
- In helping provide care or perhaps having them move into my home, what impact will that have on my family life – physically, financially, socially and emotionally?

These are NOT hypothetical questions.

These are questions you may one day need to answer.

Ageing

Ageing and later life should be and can be a very enjoyable, interesting and positive experience. People are living longer and have more activities and opportunities available to them than ever before. Whether it is increased family time or travel, interests, languages, music, a new business, sports, reading, watching movies, pets, volunteering, mentoring or one of 1000 other ways that people can enjoyably spend their time, the point is that everyone's experience of later life can be and should be a positive one. A person's sense of happiness and their overall satisfaction with life is best defined as their wellbeing.

So what is wellbeing?

There is no strict definition for 'wellbeing' because we are all different. What is shared are the factors that impact wellbeing such as a person's sense of inde-pendence, dignity, self-esteem, diet, health and mobility, housing, relation-ships with friends, family and the community, mon-ey, support, activities, opportunities and employ-ment.

An objective of this book is to ask people what wellbeing means for them and their ageing loved ones, and to provide Action Steps to help them promote and maintain this wellbeing for as long as possible.

Promoting wellbeing = actions to help create satisfaction, enjoyment and happiness.

Maintaining wellbeing = actions to help people keep what they already have.

For our ageing loved ones:

Promoting wellbeing might mean

- joining a local singing or faith group
- doing supermarket shopping online
- volunteering with a charity
- getting a new pet
- starting a new business or mentoring younger people
- inviting family and friends to visit more regularly

Maintaining wellbeing might mean

- having non-slip bath mats
- installing a grab rail in the bathtub or shower
- swimming three times a week
- maintaining a healthy, well balanced diet.
- modifying the garden so it is easier to access and maintain
- ensuring beds are age-friendly (and back-friendly)
- having a falls assessment with a GP

These are all actions that people can take to promote or maintain their wellbeing.

This book contains 297 of them.

Getting back to the questions asked at the start of the introduction, when we think about our loved ones and the impact that ageing will have, it's important to also acknowledge and try to address the negative aspects of ageing too.

These may seem extreme at this point but here are some things that you may or may not have thought about yet, with respect to your ageing loved ones:

- having difficulty dressing
- experiencing urinary incontinence
- having the skin on their leg torn open after their leg brushes against the edge of a coffee table and the bleeding not stopping for hours
- feeling dizzy and out of breath when having to walk up a flight of stairs
- having to remember to take dozens of pills every day
- forgetting their pin number at the cash machine and having no cash
- needing someone to shower them or take them to the toilet

These can all be part of daily life in our sixties, seventies, eighties, or nineties (or beyond if you are super amazing!). Everyone is different so age as a number doesn't mean anything. But as for ageing and its impacts, they are a fact of life!

One day these may be part of your loved one's or your own reality.

Looking at the bigger picture:

- today, there are 10.5 million people over sixty-five years old
- it is towards the end of our lives that we require the greatest input from health and social care services
- there will be an extra five million people joining the over sixty-fives in the next 20 years. That's 50% more people!
- the current and foreseeable financial climate demands a decrease in state support in all levels of society, compounded by relatively fewer tax payers

So the maths of that is:

Current care system under pressure

+ 50% more people over sixty-five within two decades

+ funding issues

= a big challenge for the care sector

= a big challenge for all of us

That's you included.

This is obviously not a situation where people would or should look to place blame on the older generation itself. The increase in numbers is from the baby boom years, and our current and future economic and social predicament is due to an infinite number of factors that someone better qualified can investigate elsewhere and report on. Our position is that society is where it is and it's up to all of us to do what we can to fix it.

If everyone took small, simple actions to improve their wellbeing, then that would result in a significant improvement to society and help with the solution of the challenges that the ageing population represents.

One last point...

If your ageing loved one injures themselves it will hurt them and you physically and emotionally. But the pain doesn't stop there. The arrangements before, during and after hospitalisation in terms of money, time and effort for them and their family (you) are huge and often ongoing for months – if not years or even permanently.

This is an absolute, undeniable possibility.

What can you and your loved ones do about all of this?

The good news: lots!

The sooner you:

- consider points raised in this introduction and decide which are applicable to you
- take proactive action to reduce the likelihood of injury
- take proactive action to help keep your loved ones as healthy as possible for as long as possible

The better yours and their life will be.

We also encourage people to involve their friends and family where possible across the generations because this helps to promote understanding and appreciation and a connection between the younger and older sections of society. The benefits such as children providing entertainment to their grandparents or an older neighbour being a mentor to a teenager can be felt at the personal and family level as well community and national level.

The critical philosophy

Prevention is better than cure.

A simple saying, that deserves deep thought.

Prevention is better than cure.

The further good news is that it's the objective of this book and the mission of Action for Ageing to:

1. Provide a reality check

- Are my ageing loved ones becoming more vulnerable?
- What impact does their ageing have on us both? Possibly huge!

2. Identify action steps

- Actions that you can take now to help make your ageing loved one's life safer, healthier and happier.
- Realising that prevention is not only better than cure, but it's also smarter, easier and massively cheaper.

3. Provide resources to help you take action

- Information, strategies, tips, products, services and people to help you take a proactive, positive approach to the huge challenge of care for older people that faces us all as individuals and as a society.

Another important point

People in their sixties or seventies often react to suggestions that they get a safety grab bar in the bathtub or a shower chair by saying, "But I'm not disabled".

Yes! And that's the point. They aren't. So why are they waiting until they do fall over and risk becoming disabled, before they, at the very least, get a non-slip mat for their shower?

That's crazy!

Why wait for an injury to verify vulnerability? Surely it's better to prevent an injury in the first place.

It's logical…

But, as we all know, we humans don't necessarily operate on a purely logical level. Take smoking cigarettes, bungee jumping and people who go on reality TV shows.

Our collective refusal to take seriously challenges presented by the ageing population is akin to our disregard for the 'lunatic hippies' in the 1970s and the 1980s who carried on about environmental issues, recycling and the need to separate our household rubbish into bags for plastic, paper and food scraps.

We used to regard them as freaks.

Now we're all very environmentally aware and separate our rubbish without thinking about it.

The same shift in thinking needs to happen towards care for older people and, more specifically, to people's attitudes towards taking preventative measures against injury and being proactive about safety and good health.

We should not wait for an accident to happen to prove someone is now vulnerable and only then react (when it's possibly too late).

We need to change people's mindsets about safety tips, services and products and when the best time is to introduce them.

We need to change:

- our mindset (that's you – and me too)
- our loved one's mindset
- and society's mindset too

Please read this book and keep in mind:

This book is not intended to be read from cover to cover like a novel. This book is intended to be an entertaining and useful resource that helps raise people's awareness of ageing and its potential impacts. We have sought to identify some of the opportunities and challenges that people may experience in later life and provide some helpful tips for improving older people's wellbeing.

We have covered a variety of topics in a variety of detail – there is lots left out but it is not possible to cover everything in as much detail as everyone may wish – or the book would be 10,000 pages and very difficult to fit into a handbag or coat pocket.

In this book we also encourage people to seek personal information from GPs and groups such as social services and banks for and on behalf of their ageing loved ones. This is of course, all subject to the direct approval and legal authorisation by the older person concerned.

The topics are in alphabetical order (mostly) and not order of importance. Some topics may not be relevant to you or your ageing loved ones (e.g knitting or hoarding), but FALLS for example, is a topic that is essential reading for everyone.

If you action at least one of the hundreds of tips and suggestions in this book, you will be taking a positive and proactive step towards helping make your loved one's life safer, healthier and hopefully happier too.

That's good for them.
That's good for you and your family.
And it's good for society too.

ACTION STEPS – The start

1. Read this book. ☐

2. Think about each action and your loved one.* ☐

3. Note down the action steps you want to take. ☐

4. Start to action those steps today. ☐

Prevention is **better** than cure

and SMARTER, EASIER and CHEAPER too!

* **Please note:** We use the term 'loved one' to represent family, friends or a person you are providing care to now or may likely to be in the future. We appreciate that for many people this does not necessarily always translate to having a 'loving relationship'. Indeed, your 'loved one' may in fact be a parent, friend or relative that you do not particularly get on with or know very well, but in your life journey have been called upon to help. Whatever the case, we hope the term can be interpreted to whatever is individually appropriate and that it won't distract you from the information being provided.

A question

> ## What is the telephone number of your ageing loved one's next door neighbour?

1. Double check you have your loved one's number saved in your telephone.
2. If they are home and they don't answer the telephone, can you be there or alert someone else to be there very quickly?
3. Do you know their neighbour's telephone number or someone else who can be there quickly?
4. Why not call your loved one right now and ask them for it?
5. Maybe also confirm that their neighbour has a spare key.

> **Please, do not read any further until you have their next door neighbour's telephone number saved into your mobile phone, or you have left a message requesting it.**

The above action is free, will take you less than 30 seconds to perform and yet it may be the single most important phone number you ever note down.

If you doubt this is true, ask someone who has tried to call their loved one only to find out they were lying on their floor injured and no one was able to check on them and help them in time. It's not a nice thought, but it happens. Every single day.

If obtaining a neighbour's telephone number is not an option, then perhaps they have a friend who lives nearby and you could get their telephone number instead?

ACTION STEP – Neighbour's phone number

1. Ask your loved one for their neighbour's phone number. ☐

2. Put that number into your mobile phone. ☐

3. Suggest they give their neighbour a copy of their door key. ☐

Ageing – our attitude

> **In the UK:**
>
> **Fact:** Younger people (aged 15-25) think 'old age' begins at 54.
>
> **Fact:** Older people (in their eighties) think 'old age' begins at 67.
>
> **Fact:** Whilst people in their early sixties believe that 'old age' starts at 82. That's three years AFTER the average life expectancy.

"Ageing isn't something I have to worry about … just yet"

We are all hardwired into ignoring the one inescapable fact of life – death (and the period of vulnerability and/or illness that might precede it).

We don't want to know about becoming more vulnerable.

We don't want to read about becoming more vulnerable.

And we certainly don't want to spend any time thinking about what becoming more vulnerable means for us and our loved ones.

When we think about ageing and later life for ourselves and our loved ones, we can and should be excited about it as an interesting and fulfilling period. We might consider spending time with our friends and family, being involved in activities of interest and participating in groups or travel locally, nationally or abroad. The list of fun things to do is endless.

If we do notice ageing and increasing vulnerability mentioned in a newspaper article or on television we might think:

"Thank goodness I don't have to worry about that for a few years."

We then get back to planning what's for dinner or reading about the weekend's football. Basically, just getting on with life. But sticking our heads in the sand.

The downside of ageing can be that we become more vulnerable, more prone to injury and may experience a variety of difficult challenges.

These may include some of the following:

- Needing someone to shower you or take you to the toilet.
- Watching your garden become overgrown because you can no longer do the gardening yourself, and don't have the money to pay someone else to do it.
- Experiencing deteriorating eye sight or blindness.
- Having difficulty tying your shoelaces.
- No longer being able to drive your car.
- Having urinary and/or faecal incontinence.
- Suffering severe bruising from slight touch.

- Your skin tearing when your leg brushes against the edge of a coffee table, and the bleeding not stopping for hours.
- Being unable to recall what you did yesterday or whether you have had breakfast.
- Slipping over in the bathtub and fracturing your hip.
- Needing a walking frame, which means a walk to the shops now takes 40 minutes instead of seven.
- Feeling dizzy and out of breath after walking up a flight of stairs.
- Having to take dozens of pills every day.
- Using a chair in the shower.
- Forgetting your PIN number at the cash machine.
- Being unable to read letters and bills because the writing is too small or blurry.
- Being unable to leave your home and go shopping for food and relying on meals to be delivered each day.
- Moving into family or friend's home because you can no longer live by yourself.

Yes, the reality of becoming more vulnerable and the harsher side of ageing is something we all ignore.

Ageing and later life can be and should be a wonderful period. Sadly though, it's not always nice, it's not always fun, it's not always attractive and it's not always pleasant.

And it can be expensive, it can be painful, it can be ugly and scary too.

What we are highlighting is the sooner you and your ageing loved ones recognise the potential bad bits of ageing and the simple things you can all do to help avoid or delay them, the sooner you can take action towards making their life and yours safer, healthier and happier.

As a society, if we can adjust our attitude towards ageing and improve on how we prepare for it personally and collectively, then that's to all our benefit right now, tomorrow and in the challenging years ahead of us.

ACTION STEPS – Attitude

1. Consider if a person you love is now, or may soon be vulnerable. ☐

2. Encourage action to help them live a safer life. ☐

3. Encourage action to help them live a healthier life. ☐

4. Encourage action to help them live a happier life. ☐

Alzheimer's & dementia

Fact: 820,000 people live with dementia in the UK.

Fact: Dementia costs the UK economy £23 billion per year.

Fact: That's twice the cost of cancer treatment at £12 billion per year.

Fact: There are 163,000 new cases of dementia in the UK every year. That's one every three minutes.

Fact: 50-80% of dementia cases are due to Alzheimer's disease.

Forgetfulness creeps up

Dementia is an umbrella term describing a number of diseases and conditions of the brain sharing the characteristic of decreasing brain function that are usually progressive and eventually severe. The common initial symptoms of dementia are memory loss, confusion and challenges with understanding and speech.

As the condition is progressive, with the structure and chemistry of the brain becoming more damaged over time, these initial symptoms become more severe and additional symptoms may appear, such as gradual loss of mobility, weight loss, incontinence and an increasing severity of behavioural issues (restlessness, hallucinations, agitation, wandering, suspicion and aggression).

The variety of dementia symptoms and the speed of brain deterioration experienced differs between people and the type of condition they have.

Alzheimer's is the most common form of dementia and accounts for 50-80% of dementia cases. As a person's condition becomes more severe, they will experience an increasing dependency on others for care.

Whilst there is currently no cure for dementia, there are promising developments in medication and complementary therapies which potentially slow down the rate of brain deterioration. This makes early detection and diagnosis so very important: the sooner people recognise that a loved one may be in the early stages of a form of dementia and have an assessment performed by their GP or a specialist, the greater chance there appears to be of potentially slowing the progress of their condition.

Also, by detecting dementia early, people and their families have more opportunity to prepare for the challenges ahead and provide for improved enjoyment and wellbeing for everyone.

Be aware that many families may dismiss early warning signs of dementia, such as forgetfulness, as just being part of getting old.

It's only when something alarming happens, such as your loved one disappearing from their home, that you realise there may be serious cause for concern.

With wandering, for example, quite often the person becomes totally disorientated and possibly quite agitated. A kind neighbour or an acquaintance might notice them, maybe some distance from their home and bring them back to the family. Meanwhile, the family has been frantically searching for their loved one.

If that experience turns out to be the first of many, it is a terrible and shocking introduction to an insidious and devastating brain condition.

Warning signs

There are a number of warning signs that can suggest your loved one might be in the early stages of having a brain disease such as Alzheimer's.

For example:

1. memory loss that disrupts daily life
2. challenges in planning or solving problems
3. difficulty finishing tasks at home, work or leisure
4. confusion with time or place
5. trouble understanding visual images and spatial relationships
6. new problems with words in speaking or writing
7. misplacing things and losing the ability to retrace steps
8. decreased or poor judgement
9. withdrawal from work or social activities
10. changes in mood and personality

Carer Min

Prior to my working as a carer, my husband's much loved mother used to hop on a plane to visit and would stay with us for a couple of months at a time.

During the last visit she made, we noticed that she appeared to be continually disorientated, which was highly unusual. She kept telling us that she couldn't remember where her bedroom was once she left the kitchen. We would laughingly direct her. After some days our sons took the initiative and made large paper arrows which they attached to the carpet between their grandmother's bedroom and the kitchen. This resolved the problem immediately and she happily resumed doing her 'chores' such as washing up and peeling the vegetables.

Not long after she had returned to her home we received a call to say that she had incurred a fall in her garden and had been unable to gain anyone's attention for many hours. She had broken her hip and spent some time in hospital and was then transferred to a nursing home. We were then told that she was suffering from Alzheimer's disease and that the broken hip would only hasten her demise.

As this was in the days before I had started my career as a carer for older people, neither of us had any idea about Alzheimer's disease or how it affected people, because we had lived in our own family unit bubble.

My mother-in-law deteriorated quickly, and I can remember sobbing as we left the nursing home after what, I knew, would be the last time I would see her.

Prevention

Unfortunately, the specific causes of dementia and Alzheimer's disease are still not fully understood and there are no known ways in which to categorically prevent them.

There are a number of Risk Factors that have been idenfitied that may increase a person's chances of developing a brain condition, such as age, gender, medical history and genetics. There are also lifestyle and environmental factors that are thought to potentially play a role, such as smoking, alcohol, diet, physical exercise and exposure to environments that contain high levels of substances such as metals that can potentially impair brain functioning.

People are therefore encouraged to maintain a healthy and balanced diet, to keep alcohol consumption at a reasonable level and to stop smoking. It is thought that adopting a Mediterranean-style diet can be beneficial, to help reduce saturated fat intake and manage cholesterol and blood pressure. That also means that a moderate amount of red wine consumption is actually encouraged. Yahoo! Please note the word 'moderate' though!

Once a person has been diagnosed with a form of dementia, the best that can be done (currently) is to try and reduce the pace of brain deterioration via medication, complementary and alternative therapies and lifestyle choices, and to take action to provide for their wellbeing on the road ahead.

Development of sure-fire prevention using medication is hoped for, and theories exist of a causal link between brain and heart health, early experiences of brain trauma, physical exercise and diet and dementia. One activity that has been identified as potentially helping improve or maintain brain function is the performance of mental exercises (see Topic 8, 'Brain exercises/fun' on page 72).

Unfortunately, there are no proven actions that can be taken to categorically prevent dementia. The best that can be done for now is to try and slow its progress and provide for the maintenance of the wellbeing of the person with the condition and their loved ones.

Impact

Living with or helping care for a loved one who has dementia can be extremely challenging, stressful and upsetting. As the person's mind deteriorates, their personality changes and the relationship they have with their loved ones who are caring for them changes also.

Coping with a loved one who is having hallucinations, performing repetitive movements and activities, shouting, being violent, being excessively restless, suspicious of people, hiding, following people around, experiencing sleeplessness or wandering is extremely difficult and not something people should try to deal with by themselves.

For the loved ones living with or caring for a person with dementia, the grief process is like that of a bereavement. But before the person has actually died, as they are watching the person they love disappear from them a little bit each day. This is why it is important to seek help from organisations such as Alzheimer's Society and find ways to help with the wellbeing of the person with dementia AND with the wellbeing of the loved ones who care for them.

> ### Carer Min
>
> *Whilst working as a Personal Care worker in the dementia facility at a local hostel, I was invited to organise activities for the residents, an opportunity I grabbed with both hands. Baking was a big hit. I'd gather the residents into the kitchen/dining room and discuss with them what we were going to bake. "What ingredients do we need for cheese scones, sausage rolls, sultana cakes?" The replies would fly because I was seeking information stored in their long term memories. Everyone would take a turn stirring the bowl. Whilst the item was baking we would chat about food and recipes, and then, as soon as the baking was done, the residents would all be sitting there with their cup of tea ready to launch into the goodies.*

A great program that is being encouraged around the world is a service where a trained carer is sent to live-in at the person's home when their family/regular carers need a break. This is an innovative solution to allay the distress to the older loved one, and their family, of staying in an unfamiliar environment of the care home.

Being involved in social activities like singing groups can also be of benefit to both the person with dementia and their family/ carers. Remembering song lyrics and remaining socially engaged is great exercise for people's brain, and the carers get to meet other people who can relate to their struggles as a care provider to someone with dementia.

Action

If your loved one has started to become increasingly absent-minded and displays any of the ten warning signs above, arrange an appointment with their GP for a full assessment.

The actions to help deal with and manage dementia and Alzheimer's depends on people's psychological, physical and financial circumstances. For example, how long a person with dementia might continue to live independently in their own home depends on the care that can be provided by family members.

The potential actions or strategies to help people to manage life for a person with a brain disease and help maintain their wellbeing range from the simple and inexpensive, to the more costly and technologically complex. The benefit of early diagnosis of dementia is that people have time to prepare, to find out what the condition means, what can be done for their loved one's wellbeing and then being able to take action. Having the time and capacity to do things such as drawing up a Will or Power of Attorney, before it is too late, can make a big difference to the person with dementia and their family.

Anyone concerned about Alzheimer's and dementia should immediately contact their loved one's GP. Detailed advice and information can be sought from the Alzheimer's Society via their website **www.alzheimers.org.uk** or by calling their National Dementia Helpline on **0845 300 0336** (open 8.30am to 6.30pm Monday to Friday).

> ### Carer Min
>
> *When the father of one family started wandering, the family was on tenterhooks, worrying about when he would next disappear.*
>
> *The father always left by the front door, and would be found disoriented, hours later, several streets from the house.*
>
> *With a flash of inspiration, the family stuck a 'Ladies Toilet' sign on the inside of the front door. Being a traditional gentelmen, he never opened that door again.*

Practical tools

Assistive Technology is where a product enables or helps enable someone to do a task that they would otherwise have been unable to do or helps keep them safer. Such products can help where a person may be experiencing a deterioration in their eyesight, hearing, speech, memory, strength, sleep, dressing, toileting, socialising and mobility. Products can be used in the home to help remind people with dementia to take their medication, eat meals, turn off their oven and even lock their front door before going to bed.

Where an ageing loved one may be at risk of wandering from their home, some examples of various products that may be able to help prevent an accident or help manage the risk of wandering are:

Personal alarm

A personal alarm can be discreetly attached to a loved one who is at risk of wandering, so if they leave the house an alarm will sound.

Door sensor

Programmable door sensors can be placed around the home so that if an exit door in the house is opened, you will be immediately notified by an alarm.

GPS locator

A wide range of personal GPS locators are now available, offering different tracking and notification services. Before buying, it's always good to seek the advice of your loved one's GP and perhaps a professional telecare supplier to determine the best product for your needs and budget.

Carer Min

A friend visited his mother in a locked dementia facility one day, and as he arrived at the gate, a beautifully groomed lady, complete with hat and handbag, approached from the other side. Thinking she had been a visitor, he opened the security gate for her and stood aside to let her pass.

When the staff discovered a resident was missing they asked if anyone had seen her. "Oh, yes, I let her out through the gate", my friend responded. The place went into meltdown, and the lady was located by the police on the other side of the city.

It is worth noting that funding may be available to assist in paying for telecare products, via social services, a charity, housing associations or other means if the eligibility criteria of the funding source is met.

Using such devices may seem a bit extreme and intrusive to many people who aren't yet performing a caring role, or don't have a wandering loved one they're concerned about. But if you have ever raced around the streets, desperately looking for someone, you will fully appreciate any idea or service that might prevent their disappearance or help with their safe return the next time they unexpectedly head out the door.

It's always worth sitting back and trying to think of ideas (like the LADIES TOILET sign) that can be effective, simple and inexpensive.

For more information about the variety of Assistive Technology and telecare products available please refer to the Topic – Telecare/ Technology in this book. You can also contact the Alzheimer's Society for information and support about Alzheimer's disease and dementia.

If you would like more information about dementia and actions that can help with maintaining wellbeing such as physical exercise, brain exercise or assistive technology products, please refer to your loved one's GP.

You can also contact the Alzheimer's Society for information and support about Alzheimer's disease and dementia via their website **www.alzheimers.org.uk** and helpline **0845 300 0336** (open 8.30am to 6.30pm Monday to Friday).

We also have additional information and links available on the Resources page on our website: **www.ActionForAgeing.com/ Resources**.

Remember:

Although a topic in this book may not be relevant to you today, please read it anyway, because it may be part of your reality in the future.

ACTION STEPS – Alzheimer's & dementia

1. Why not print out and show the list of warning signs of dementia to your family and friends, so they are aware of what to look out for? ☐

2. Consider making an appointment with a doctor if your loved one displays any of the warning signs on an increasingly regular basis. ☐

3. Visit Alzheimer's Society website or call their helpline for more information about what dementia is and the resources, support and services that are available to help people with the condition and their loved ones. ☐

4. Consider the Risk Factors and encourage positive diet and lifestyle choices. ☐

5. Where a loved one is diagnosed with dementia, encourage information gathering and taking a proactive approach towards maintaining wellbeing. ☐

6. Investigate the alternatives for medication, complementary therapies, lifestyle choices, assistive technologies, activities and even lateral thinking solutions (such as Ladies Toilet sign on the back of the front door) that can help slow the progress of the disease or improve wellbeing. ☐

7. Remember that wonderful help is available from charities such as Alzheimer's Society. ☐

Banking

> **Fact:** Women aged under sixty-five use cashpoints 72 times a year
>
> **Fact:** Women aged over sixty-five use cashpoints 11 times a year
>
> **Fact:** Only 16% of over sixty-five use internet banking

Banks and banking can be a challenge

If you find it annoying dealing with your bank and money matters, imagine how your loved ones who didn't grow up with computers, cash machines and online financial management may feel. Exactly.

If your loved one is a silver surfer and can make transfers and pay bills via the internet, that's great. But the majority (84%)

don't use online banking so wouldn't know their bank's website even if it put on a large, silly hat and introduced itself. The over sixty-fives conduct their banking the traditional way, by walking into their local branch and dealing with financial matters over the counter with the cashier.

So if you start taking the action of a carer:

- sit down with your loved one
- go through what bills they pay at the bank each month
- arrange for as many direct debits as possible to be set up
- aim to substantially reduce the frequency and duration of their visits to the bank

A helpful system is to have one box in the kitchen that contains household bills.

This makes it easier to organise what can be paid automatically by direct debit and what can be paid over the counter on the next bank visit.

It's worth following through on this simple step. Many carers might get one or two bills automated, but neglect less regular bills or charges. Ask yourself instead: "What else can be sorted by direct debit?" Once you have organised your loved one's finances, add a list to your bill box in the kitchen so everyone knows what's going on.

Research indicates that older people find cashpoints stressful. For example, sixty-five year olds use cash machines 72 times a year on average, while the over sixty-fives in general use cash machines 11 times a year. Along with the risk of being attacked from behind and robbed, there is the more common anxiety of remembering their PIN, especially when there is a queue of people waiting. Adding to this stress is that people have been repeatedly told to NEVER write their PIN down or carry it with them.

To help alleviate this stress:

- Make sure your loved one's PIN number has been changed to the year of their wedding anniversary, birth year of their first child or some other historical date of personal significance.

This is because once people reach a certain point, their long term memory might be clearer than their short term memory. You can ask them what the weather was like on their twenty-first birthday and they will bore you with a half hour meteorological report, complete with wavy circle diagrams. But ask them what they had for breakfast, they may not be too sure.

Carer Min

I have met quite a few older people who have an inherent distrust of the banks dating back to their experiences during the Depression. Therefore they tend to hoard substantial sums within their own home.

This practice has always alarmed me and other carers I have encountered who have experienced this situation. Upon advising my management, the manager contacts members of the family who may or may not be aware of this situation.

Where dementia clients are involved, families have undergone discreet searches and large sums have been found in amazing places, such as inside a cuckoo clock or where a roll of thousands of pounds was hidden in a shoe at the front door. Bags of notes have been found in the hallway manhole, stuffed in the sofa cushion or buried in the garden. They might be getting old, but your loved one's imagination for hiding places is razor sharp. It's just remembering where they hid the money that causes the loved one's and the carer's anxiety.

Many years ago my husband's uncle passed away and his family, who lived a great distance away, rang and asked if we would go to his house and conduct a search, because they knew that he had hidden money and it would be a week before they arrived in town.

Well, it was like a treasure hunt! We located money in the ceiling, under the carpet and many other places in between. At the end of the day we'd rounded up £18,000. In 1968!

When the rest of the family arrived a week later they found even more.

Older people are vulnerable and very trusting (as was the way of their youth). Unfortunately the world is quite different now, so the responsibility falls on us carers to keep them safe and make sure that money is not left lying around.

There was also a delightful gentleman, Joseph, whom I regularly visited. One day I walked into his kitchen and he had taken out his cutlery drawer. He'd worked as a cabinet maker and surprised me when he reached into the cavity and produced a secret drawer into which he added a wad of notes to an already substantial pile. He was not at all perturbed that I had observed him doing this, which somewhat concerned me. I advised my manager and she advised the family.

I don't feel I am making people more vulnerable by mentioning all this here, as unfortunately the secret is out within the thieves' community.

Quite a few years ago I had the pleasure of working with a wonderful gentleman, Sam. Sam was to offer me words which took a tremendous load off my shoulders. I was constantly trying to think of ways I could rebuild my bank account, resulting in my stepping out of the socialising scene and simply living a very boring, dreary life.

I remember I made a throw away remark to Sam, telling him there weren't enough hours in the week for me to work and build a nest egg. Sam stepped towards me and stated, "Min, shrouds don't have pockets."

Sam's wise words to me were a great gift, that I have always remembered. From that day forward I have stopped fretting about money, relaxed and started meeting friends again, even shouting them a coffee when I've had the wherewithal.

I often wish that older people would treat themselves occasionally, rather than tenaciously holding onto their money. Most heirs would have preferred their parents to have spent their money freely on their own comfort, rather than saving it to pass on to the children.

In taking action for your loved one and their banking needs you should:

- confirm they are okay for you to become involved in their financial affairs
- identify what you can do now to simplify their current arrangements
- look at what their future dealings are likely to be and take action now to sort those out
- remember, it's easier to make complicated arrangements when everyone is in good health than after someone becomes ill or starts suffering the effects of ageing

ACTION STEPS – reorganise banking

1. Find out how they currently do their banking. ☐

2. Identify what payments can be automated. ☐

3. Find out what they find stressful and how those matters can be resolved. ☐

4. Ask "what future banking activities can be arranged today?" ☐

5. Save their PIN as a memorable year. ☐

6. Discourage them from keeping large quantities of cash in the house. ☐

7. Make sure their cash at home is kept out of sight of windows. ☐

8. Get a shoebox for the bills in the kitchen and review it. ☐

9. Shrouds don't have pockets – so persuade your loved one to treat themselves today! ☐

Bathroom safety

Amongst the 10.4 million over 65s in the UK each year:

Fact: There are 3.4 million reported falls.

Fact: There are an estimated extra 10 million falls that go unreported.

Fact: The bathroom is the most frequent location of domestic injury (70%).

Fact: Bath seats start from a price of £30

Fact: Hip replacements start from a price of £12,500*

*That is just for the standard medical bit. The actual cost physically, financially and emotionally to the injured and their friends and family is considerably more.

Hot + wet + slippery = danger

Everyone likes stepping out of the shower or bath onto a comfy bath mat and our ageing loved ones are no exception. However, comfy doesn't necessarily mean safe and these seemingly innocent little pieces of material can be lethal. The bathroom can be a dangerous place for people of all ages, but especially so for the eldest amongst us.

In the UK alone there are 3.4 million reported falls by the over sixty-fives every year (with 2,500 deaths directly from the fall). And the bathroom is the most common location for accidents (with 70% of domestic injuries).

For people over 80, more than 50% suffer a reported fall every year.

So how many near falls occur?

That number is also going to be millions.

The simple fact is that when people are in the bathroom, the surfaces around them are all wet, slippery and hard. They are at much greater risk of slipping over and hurting themselves than when they are standing in the kitchen, fully clothed, reading a newspaper.

Many factors can impact bathroom safety and if people take some simple steps they can help improve their chances of staying upright and injury-free. For example, whilst bright lighting is always encouraged throughout the house, in the bathroom it is useful to avoid clear bulbs that may cause glare from the various shiny and wet surfaces. This can affect spatial awareness and judgement about distance, leading to your loved one misjudging their step from the bathtub and causing them to slip over. It is therefore a good idea to use a frosted bulb that is at the maximum wattage for a fitting so that people can benefit from the brightest non-glare light as possible. Or if a clear bulb is used, to have a frosted light shade.

To avoid the potential risk of falling when reaching for a dropped bar of soap, instead use liquid soap squeezed from a bottle and a large sponge or cloth for washing. If any of these items are dropped, they are much easier to pick up and are much less of a slip risk than a wet bar of soap zooming around a person's feet. It is also a good idea to keep the bathroom floor as dry as possible. Be mindful of spilling products such as talcum powder as:

Talcum powder + shiny bathroom floor = ice skating rink.

Carer Min

We are all creatures of habit and generally resistant to change, whether it is supposed to be good or bad for us. So, trying to encourage loved ones to get bath mats or replace their current ones if they are in poor condition can require a substantial amount of diplomacy.

Bathmats

To reduce the risk of an impromptu Seniors Skating Display, it's definitely worth investing in a good quality, non-slip bath mat for inside and outside of the bathtub. Make sure you test the new bath mat in your loved one's bathroom, to reassure yourself that it will remain securely in place. There are plenty of mats out there that claim to be non-slip and yet provide only a relatively small degree of actual slip resistance.

A common reason people don't want to get a bath mat for inside their bath tub is because the mat needs to be cleaned every couple of weeks to prevent mildew build-up. It goes a bit green underneath in parts and looks a bit manky. This might be true, sometimes. But given the quality of cleaning products available nowadays and the one minute of scrubbing it takes twice a month to substantially improve the household's bathroom safety, it is one minute well spent!

Or looking at it another way, twenty-four minutes a year for the opportunity of non-slip bathing.

Twenty-four minutes of scrubbing a year (which is good exercise in itself) will certainly seem like a bargain in hindsight if you or a loved one does slip over and hurt themselves. Not forgetting that hundreds of thousands of people in the UK do slip over in the bath tub every year. Quite likely millions.

Remember:

A few extra pounds spent now on a new, high quality bath mat for inside and outside of the bath or shower is a lot cheaper than paying the bill for weeks in a hospital and possibly a new hip!

Bath seating

It's better to sit than stand

Great seating products that help improve bathing safety include bath seats, bath boards/benches, bath lifts and transfer benches. A wide variety of bath seats are available: a simple plastic seat with suction pads or rubber feet on the legs to stop the chair from slipping; a padded seat with spider-like arms that securely wedge it against the walls and over the edge of the bath; a seat that folds down from the wall; or seats that are raised and secured

across the width of the bathand with a swivel function to provide bath entry and exit from a seated position. Bath boards/benches are a board that is secured to and sits across the width of the bath. These also come in a very wide variety of styles and functions, with some equipped with side handles to assist people to sit down or stand up. Others may extend outside of the bath and have legs onto the bathroom floor to help the user transfer to and from the bath. There are also bath lifts that work with hydraulics and bathing cushions that are inflated by a motor, to raise and lower people on a seat into their bath.

There are so many different varieties of bath seating to meet people's individual needs that it is definitely worth spending some time investigating what works best for now or keeping in mind the options for when your ageing loved ones are in the market for a seat in the future.

Please encourage them not to wait until after they have had a fall, before recognising that a product like a bath seat or bath bench is needed.

The statistics are that 70% of accidents in the home happen in the bathroom. Many are caused because a person has been affected in the shower by the heat, by dizziness or simply lost their balance in the wet and slipped over.

Two statements to consider:

1. Installing a bath seat or bath bench will help reduce the risk of injury in the bath (or shower).
2. Dancing in a pair of six inch stilettos in the bath or shower will help increase the risk of injury.

Both of these statements are correct and both are quite obvious. However, only one of the above is actually acknowledged and acted upon.

(Hint – it's not the bath seat.)

Remember:

Many of the topics we discuss may seem extreme and irrelevant now, but it's good to read about them anyway because they may well be part of your reality tomorrow.

Shower seating

Shower stalls can often be quite confined. This, coupled with heat and rising steam, can be a recipe for dizziness. If a shower seat is available when dizziness strikes, people are definitely reducing their risk of shower injury.

The main varieties of shower seating tend to be variations of:

- **shower seats:** like a modern dining chair, usually made of plastic or metal or a combination thereof

- **shower chairs:** like a slimmed down, waterproof wheel chair and some come with a commode seat built in

- **shower stools:** not unsurprisingly, much like a stool and also made of plastic and/or metal

All three types of shower seating come in a wide variety of shapes and sizes, some triangular-seated for fitting snugly into the corner of the shower, or fold up versions, some with handles, some with backs, whilst some fold down from the wall.

Seats with extendable legs are also available, so that the height setting can be arranged for maximum ease and minimum effort for the user.

One important feature to look out for in any stool or chair is rubber tips on the feet, to help provide maximum grip. It is also worth noting that the varieties with handles are popular with older people because they provide the person with something to hang onto whilst lowering or raising themselves.

There are even wheeled types if a loved one is struggling to walk into the bathroom. That means they can be wheeled from their bedroom into the bathroom and even directly into the shower if it's an open walk-in type, without having to stand up. This is a much safer way to bathe if mobility is an issue and helps avoid a lot of effort and stress for the older person and their carer (possibly you).

Some bathrooms have a separate shower and bathtub. Others have a shower head above one end of the bath and your loved one therefore has to climb over the side of the bath in order to stand in it for a shower. Others might also have a Jacuzzi, sauna and large flat screen TV.

However your loved one's current bathroom is set up, there is a good chance that with a few simple changes or additions, their bathing can become a lot safer.

Bathroom tips list

- non-slip bath mats inside and outside the bathtub and shower recess
- grab rails installed along the wall of the bathtub or in the shower cubicle and next to the toilet too (might as well make the most of the professional installer whilst they in the house!)
- keep the bathroom floor clean and dry
- plug in nightlights in the bathroom and in the hallway between the bathroom and the bedroom
- replace the bar of soap in the bath and shower with a large squeezy-bottle of liquid soap and a large sponge. Both are much easier to pick up if dropped and much less of a slip risk than a bar of soap spinning around on the floor

- plan enough time for showering/bathroom activity as rushing is a frequent cause of falls around the home

- avoid using a screen door to clutch for stability to enter and exit the shower or bathtub, as they are not designed to take a person's bodyweight

- remove bath or shower fixtures that are not safety items, to prevent them being used instead of a grab rail, in the event of a slip. For example, whilst slipping, a person may grab at a towel ring as a reflex and instead of it remaining fixed, the person, the towel ring and a number of broken tiles all end up in a pile on the floor of the bathtub

- in the bathroom, use frosted bulbs that have the maximum wattage to ensure the most light and least glare is generated

A printable version of this list and all of our safety lists are available on the Resources page of our website: **www.ActionForAgeing.com/resources**

What's important is for people to take action and:

- check out all the bath mat and seating varieties available

- consider seeking professional medical or healthcare advice on which seat might be most suitable

- don't wait until an accident occurs to verify a loved one's vulnerability

Where possible, it is worth considering seeking the advice of an unbiased, professional expert on daily living equipment such as an occupational therapist (OT). This is especially so if looking at the more expensive items such as powered bath chairs that can cost hundreds of pounds.

The cost of a personal assessment and the purchase of the products themselves might be paid for privately by the user, or funding may be available from another source such as their housing association (if the person lives in a HA property), their care home (if the person is a resident and it is in the scope of their service agreement), their insurance company or a charity or organisation that helps older people in need.

It also might be helpful for your loved one to visit their local Disabled Living Centre, where they can see many of the products, try out what appeals, and receive clear, impartial advice. Some even have an in-store OT, with whom they could make an appointment. Otherwise, it might be worth arranging for the OT who completed their assessment to accompany them to the centre. A very sensible investment!

As a present to your ageing loved ones, why not arrange for a private home safety assessment? They may laugh at first and reassure you that it isn't necessary, "we're not that old", but it might just be the best present you ever give them. Even if they don't action anything now, it may help raise their awareness, which can only be a good thing for their long term wellbeing.

The cost of the assessment and recommended products might even be shared amongst other friends and family. Why not suggest it and see what they think?

Where purchasing products is concerned, especially when over the internet, the person needs to know their weight, height and seat dimension before doing so, otherwise the product may be delivered and be unsuitable. If this is the case, the bath seat may end up in the corner of the spare bedroom, next to the unused exercise bike, mini trampoline, bread maker and fondue set.

How to contact an occupational therapist (OT):

- by self-referral to the local council occupational therapy department
- by referral from a GP
- via a charity or
- directly through an independent OT service provider

For information on how to confirm if an OT is professionally registered with the Health Professions Council (HPC) or for other occupational therapy services and contact details, please visit our website Resources page: **www.ActionForAgeing.com/ resources**

Please note that the regulations, processes, government departments, organisations, contacts and terminology regarding health care provision and service providers are constantly changing so the information provided here is intended to be for general awareness purposes only.

For the latest details regarding the assessment, provision and funding of home safety products and services and the contact details for Disabled Living Centres, please visit our website Resources page: **www.ActionForAgeing.com/resources**

Carer min

If the reason for not getting a bath seat is saving money, then that person needs to do their sums again. Any fall by a frail person in the bathroom has enormous potential for serious injury. All the surfaces are often wet and always hard.

Not surprisingly, it's only after a fall that many people will invest in a shower seat.

We humans are odd like that.

If you would like information about bath seating and other bathroom safety products and suppliers, please refer to the Resources page on our website: **www.ActionForAgeing.com/ resources**

ACTION STEPS – Bathroom safety

1. Check that your loved ones are using a quality, non-slip bath mat for inside and outside of the bath tub. ☐

2. Check the lighting in the bathroom is bright and the bulbs are non-glare. ☐

3. Investigate having grab bars installed in the bath tub, shower and next to the toilet. ☐

4. Find out about bath or shower seating and ideally make a purchase before a potentially avoidable accident occurs. ☐

5. Ask your loved one's doctor which bath seating may be the most appropriate. ☐

6. Recommend they follow their doctor's advice. ☐

7. Visit a local Disabled Living Centre and check out what products are available. ☐

8. Find out if funding is available from one of the sources described. ☐

9. Consider having an occupational therapist perform a home assessment and see what safety items or home modifications they recommend for now and in the future. ☐

10. Encourage your family and friends to do the same. ☐

Topic 6

Bedroom safety

> **Fact:** There are two main risk factors contributing to back injury among nurses:
> 1. Transferring patients
> 2. Bed making
>
> **Fact:** Starting price for a bed rail = £60
>
> **Fact:** Cost of a restaurant dinner for two with starters = £60
>
> **Fact:** Average duration of a restaurant dinner = two hours
>
> **Fact:** Number of times a bedrail is used over three years = 2,190

Bed equipment – Being stuck and without help

We spend most of our lives finding an excuse to stay all warm and snug in our beds, but we generally know that if we want to climb out and face the new day, it's an easy action of feet to the floor, bum off the bed and a big stretch and yawn for good measure.

One of the side effects of ageing however, can be a decrease in strength and agility. This can mean that for some, getting up out of bed can be very difficult.

The reason for this can be as a result of injury, excess weight, medication or simply due to the effects of time on our body.

If your loved one is finding it a struggle to get out of their bed, a bed rail support handle can be attached under the base and up beside each side of the mattress to help provide the required leverage. The metal bar can then be gripped while they manoeuvre themselves out of bed.

By that description, bed rails may sound like some sort of complicated gym machine that also does your tax return and makes a very good traditional espresso. In reality, bed rails are very simple fittings that provide great support.

Bed rails are designed to help reduce the risk of your ageing loved one being stranded in bed because they are unable to mobilise. All they need to do is grab the rail handle for support and get out of bed in the usual manner.

If they are from a circus background and their usual manner of rising from the bed is doing a double back flip into a cannon and firing themselves across the room, maybe you should forget the bed rail and install a trapeze instead.

Along with bedrails, other bedroom equipment that can assist people are bed risers that lift the bed to a height for easier access, bed trays that can roll in across the lap of someone sitting up in bed, bed guards to help prevent someone from accidentally rolling out of bed, mattress protectors for dust mite or bed bug infestations and mattress raisers/tilters that can help reduce the over-stretching of muscles and tendons, especially where hip problems are present.

These are just a few examples of the many types of equipment that are available to assist older people in the bedroom. For more ideas and information about products, please refer to the topic Gadgets and aid items in this book and also the Resources page on our website: **www.ActionForAgeing.com/resources**

Remember:

Many of the topics we discuss may seem extreme and irrelevant now, but it's good to read about them anyway because they may well be part of your reality tomorrow.

BED POSITIONING –
Don't just make it – move it

Something as simple as making the bed can be absolute dynamite for people's backs.

Oddly, we don't seem to pay much attention to where a bed is placed, until we injure ourselves making it.

For your loved ones, twenty years ago, the bed being in the corner against the wall provided more usable bedroom space and the hassle of making the bed was seen as an acceptable trade-off. That was fine for then.

Now, however, they may be less agile and having the bed against the wall causes difficulties. If so, move with the times, and move the bed so it's easier to access.

Carer Min

I recall visiting a gentleman who lived in a caravan and I was instructed to make his bed each visit. It sounded okay, but in reality it was a difficult chore.

The bed was placed against the back wall of the caravan. Each end was jammed against the sides of the caravan. The only way to tackle this task was to crawl all over the mattress, lifting the mattress corners and sides in order to secure the bed linen.

My back was screaming with the strain! How I managed to make that bed for months without putting my back out is one of life's true mysteries.

Note: A quick test to check if a loved one's bed is at the correct height:

When sitting on the edge of their bed, the soles of their feet should be just touching the floor. From there, it should then be easy for them to stand. If not, the bed height may need to be adjusted.

In everyone's interest, it's worth trying to ensure that beds are in a back-friendly position.

The best position for a bed is in the middle of the wall, or at least in a central location, so that the person making it can manoeuvre around it and make it without any unnecessary strain on the body.

When you're a spring chicken, it rarely matters whether you are flat out on a futon on the floor, dangling from a hammock, getting seasick in a waterbed or banging your head on the ceiling above the top bunk. You will always manage to get in and out of bed without fuss.

When it comes to older people however, the spring may have left the chicken and if their bed is too low, then falling into and out of bed becomes the only option.

And a bad one at that.

A key factor in helping our loved one's maintain their independence is by helping them remain injury-free and mobile.

If your loved one's bedroom is no longer suitable for a person of their age and health, maybe it's time to consider moving their whole bedroom somewhere more appropriate?

If they have to go up flights of stairs and are showing signs of being unsteady on their feet, why not pack up their bedroom and move it somewhere more convenient downstairs?

Carer Min

Over the years as a carer I have come across many beds with one long side placed flush against the wall. Being in someone else's house, I had two choices.

First choice: Climb around on top of the bed, endeavouring to lift the sides of the mattress so that I could tuck the sheets and blankets under.

Second choice: Move the bed to one side, make the bed and then move the bed back again.

Neither appealed to me because my back was at major risk.

Above all, as a carer in any capacity, you need to respect and look out for your back and that of your loved one.

A question worth considering or raising with your ageing loved one:

Is their bedroom in a suitable place?

If yes, that's great. If not, perhaps it's time for a change?

Do you really want to wait until after an accident before making the move?

Resistance to change is normal, for all of us.

But sometimes, a change is necessary.

If your loved one's bed is in a sensible location but they have difficulty getting in and out, or they're struggling to move around once they're in it, they may benefit from having bed devices or bed raisers installed. With regard to equipment, it is the advice of the occupational therapist and recommendations in their assessment that you should look to action. The installation of any equipment should only ever be carried out by a trained technician.

If health and injury-risk considerations deem it necessary that your loved one should move downstairs on a permanent basis, an occupational therapist will be required to provide advice on a suitable bed location and the toileting and washing facility options. Perhaps a shower cubicle or toilet can be installed where a cupboard currently is?

Whatever the modification might be, it's best to arrange a joint site visit by a reputable building company rep and your loved one's occupational therapist. This ensures that any home modifications you have in mind will meet building and health and safety regulations.

Bedroom tips list

- if getting into and out of bed is a challenge, consider getting a bed rail installed
- if a bed is too low, then bed raisers can help bring the bed up to a more accessible height
- ensure a bed is in a central position so that it can be made without undue stress on the bed-maker's back
- keep the bedroom floor and walkways clear of clutter
- have a working flashlight in a drawer next to the bed in case of power failure

- discourage loved ones from wearing too-long pyjama bottoms or night gowns that reach the floor and may be tripped over
- never smoke in bed
- check out what bedroom products are available, as there may be one that helps improve wellbeing (e.g. mattress tilters) that you may not be aware of
- have a telephone in the bedroom, in case of an emergency
- have a bedside lamp and nightlights between the bedroom and the bathroom
- avoid having electrical cords anywhere that they can be tripped over
- avoid having bed linen or bedspreads that touch the floor as they also represent a fall hazard
- install dual smoke and monoxide alarm to ceiling outside bedroom

A printable version of this list and all of our safety lists are available on the Resources page of our website: **www.ActionForAgeing.com/resources**

Where purchasing products is concerned, especially when over the internet, the exact requirements of the user and specifications of the product need to be very clearly understood. Otherwise the product may be delivered and found to be unsuitable. If this is the case, the new bed raisers may end up in the corner of the spare bedroom, next to the unused exercise bike, mini trampoline, bread maker, fondue set and wrong-sized bath seat.

How to contact an occupational therapist (OT):

- by self-referral to the local council occupational therapy department
- by referral from a GP
- via a charity or
- directly through an independent OT service provider

For information on how to confirm if an OT is professionally registered with the Health Professions Council (HPC) or for other occupational therapy services and contact details, please visit our website Resources page: **www.ActionForAgeing.com/resources**

Please note that the regulations, processes, government departments, organisations, contacts and terminology regarding health care provision and service providers are constantly changing so the information provided here is intended to be for general awareness purposes only.

For the latest details regarding the assessment, provision and funding of home safety products and services and the contact details for Disabled Living Centres, please visit our website Resources page: **www.ActionForAgeing.com/resources**

ACTION STEPS – Bedroom Safety

1. Print out the Bedroom Safety Tips list and share it with friends and family. ☐

2. Find out what bed rail and bed equipment is available. ☐

3. Check the bed is in a central position so you can make it from the sides. ☐

4. Suggest to your loved one that they may consider having an occupational therapist visit to assess their bedroom (and household) for safety recommendations. ☐

5. Consider making some or all of the modifications, like moving a bedroom to a location with easier access. ☐

6. Remind family and friends that everything doesn't have to be done at once. A gradual approach can be easier physically, emotionally and financially. ☐

TOPIC 7

Books

> **Fact:** Four per cent of books in the UK are available in large fonts for the visually impaired.
>
> **Fact:** The Royal National Institute of Blind People (RNIB) has 20,000 audio book titles available.

Go LARGE (print) or audio book

Many older people stop reading books, after a lifetime of being a reader, because they have difficulty reading small print.

This is an entirely understandable, yet avoidable situation, as there are many books available in large print or as audio books.

If your loved one does not wish to read books because they've lost interest, then that's fine. But if they want to read books, but can't due to failing eyesight, then there are alternatives available.

Whilst only 4% of books in the UK are published with fonts for the visually impaired, a great many are available as audio books.

To find large print and audio books, you can go to:

- the RNIB and other sight-related charities
- your local library
- high street retailers or specialist visual impairment book shops
- online book retailers

Most of literature's classic works are available as audio books, as are many of the latest best sellers.

There's certainly something for everyone.

Audio books today are often presented and read by famous actors, who sound like they are in the library of a majestic manor house, seated in an ancient leather arm chair beside a huge fireplace, reading to you personally by the light of the roaring fire.

The fact that they might actually have made the recording in a cold little studio on an industrial estate in Watford is completely irrelevant. Audio books these days sound great and there are loads of them!

More audio book facts

- About 40% of audio books are borrowed from public libraries.
- There are specific audio book charities that create and distribute their own recordings, either in the post or via internet streaming.
- The BBC is the largest audio book publisher.
- As well as the usual titles of fiction and non-fiction audio books, you should also keep in mind the huge selection of additional audio material now on the market.

While it's handy if your loved one has a portable music device (such as an MP3 player) and can download their favourite content from four corners of the globe, it's possible they're not quite that high tech.

Instead, your loved one may have only progressed as far as owning a CD player (circa 1991). Don't worry; that's all they need for an infinite range of audio entertainment options.

For example, there are huge swathes of old radio shows that have been put into CD gift packs. There are comedies, talk shows, variety acts and even famous speeches of the twentieth century if that's your loved one's fancy.

To find out more about specific suppliers of large print books, audio books and other sources of audio entertainment as well as special products such as headphones and amplifiers for people with hearing impairments, please visit the Resources page on our website: **www.ActionForAgeing.com/Resources**

ACTION STEPS – Books

1. Check if your loved one has any difficulty reading and if so, suggest they have an eye check. ☐

2. Find out what your loved one's favourite books, authors and topics are. ☐

3. Put a list together of the large print books that are of interest. ☐

4. Buy or borrow a large print book and see if your loved one is able to read it with greater ease. ☐

5. If they still find reading a book with large font difficult or tiresome then they may like to try an audio book instead. ☐

6. If you don't have any luck on the book front, you might find out from your loved one what their favourite radio show or variety show is from when they were growing up, as you may be able to source a recording for them online. ☐

ACTION NOTES – Book titles, authors, topics

Topic 8

Brain exercises/fun

You may have heard the phrase "the brain is a muscle that needs to be exercised".

This is only half correct.

The brain isn't a muscle, it's an organ. But it is like a muscle, in the sense that the more frequently we stimulate the brain, the more it grows.

Without digging too deeply into complex biology, it's a recognised medical fact that when we learn new information or activities, the prefrontal cortex in the brain receives exercise. The increase in stimulation from having to think helps create and maintain a cognitive or brain reserve.

The reason this is critical for people as they age, is that the prefrontal cortex is the part of the brain that is known to weaken the most, as people age.

Not only is the prefrontal cortex directly linked to a person's personality and intelligence, but it is also critical for decision making, maintaining perspective between current and future events, engagement and etiquette with others and being able to analyse their thoughts rationally.

Most importantly, studies around the world have shown that keeping their brain active and their brain reserves topped up may help diminish a person's risk of Alzheimer's and dementia.

In short, keeping our brain active won't guarantee people can avoid diminished mental capacity or avoid a brain disease, such as dementia, but it may well improve our chances of avoiding it and staying mentally sharp for longer.

That's a pretty good reason for your loved ones to start thinking about brain exercises/fun!

So what type of brain exercises/fun are there?

You may have heard of many of these exercises but the critical part is to try and ensure that your ageing loved ones actually perform the activity or exercise on a regular basis.

Regular activities that are good for brain exercise/fun include:

- reading
- learning a language
- card games (memory-based)
- creating and maintaining a scrap book
- chess
- learning or using a computer
- writing a diary
- knowledge/trivia games
- crosswords and sudoku
- visiting museums and galleries
- learning an instrument
- learning new song lyrics

> ## Carer Min
>
> *I regularly play Scrabble with a lovely lady who has dementia. Although she is unable to recall what was said ten minutes ago, when she sits down in front of a Scrabble board she is an expert player. Words one has never heard of are placed on the board and sure enough, they are in the dictionary. Her short term memory might be a bit short, but her long term memory is amazing.*

Some activities you may not be aware of that can turn ordinary daily tasks into fantastic brain exercises/fun are:

Memorising the shopping list

- Spend a few minutes writing a shopping list, then create an order or system to remember the number of items. This is a great activity to stimulate the brain.

- To reinforce the list, your loved one can recall it on their way to the shops and then once they are there.

- Turning the shopping list into a memory game is easy, free and a regular activity.

- A written copy of the list can always be taken in the back pocket, in case of emergency.

Using odd hand for daily tasks

A fantastic way to stimulate brain activity and turn ordinary, mundane tasks into something more interesting is by encouraging your ageing loved ones to use their odd hand for performing daily tasks.

If they are usually right-handed, suggest they try using their left hand to:

- brush teeth
- brush hair
- open mail
- write down notes or shopping lists
- dial the phone
- use the computer mouse
- prepare dinner (will make knives more exciting – please take care!)
- eat dinner with fork and knife switched around
- wash and dry dishes

Shaving (with a blade anyway) is probably best kept as normal, as waving one of those about may be a recipe for a disaster.

By using the other hand, all of the above activities become more challenging and require your ageing loved ones to think and concentrate rather than using motions that are habitual and automatic.

Why not try it for yourself? It makes brushing teeth (almost) fun!

Computer games

Gone are the days when computer games are just for spotty teenagers. A large and growing part of the computer gaming industry is now focused on the older part of the market. The games are based on both traditional, popular games (such as Sudoku) as well as completely new games focusing on memory, analysis and speed.

What is very helpful is that the gaming industry have analysed the various studies to identify what activities might be most beneficial for improving brain activity and then built engaging and entertaining games to encourage it.

The games are based on challenges to enhance memory and improve concentration, doing fun things such as playing short piano pieces, unscrambling words and figuring out maths equations. They are intended to be performed each day (in short 5-10 minute sessions) and a log of the player's performance is usually able to be stored in the memory of the game machine. That way people can track their performance over time and hopefully see an improvement.

Furthermore, not only are the computer games able to offer a massive variety of challenges, they also have the option for people to gradually increase the difficulty of the game they are playing as their skill level improves. By doing so, people are gradually having to think and act faster, which provides a great stimulus to brain activity.

A great side effect of brain exercises/fun is an increase in confidence!

Using as many of your senses as possible

Another great tip is to encourage your ageing loved one to use as many of their sense as they can, whilst performing daily tasks.

This means maybe closing their eyes and listening to all the sounds whilst eating their breakfast, humming whilst reading the newspaper, singing in the shower, reciting poetry whilst weeding the garden, eating a banana with their eyes shut or playing music whilst washing dishes.

Along with the usual five suspects on the senses front (sight, hearing, taste, smell and touch) there are also a variety of others including balance, acceleration, temperature, pain and one called the kinaesthetic sense. An example of a kinaesthetic sense is where someone is asked to close their eyes and touch the tip of their nose. They therefore have no other sense than their kinaesthetic sense to guide their finger.

PERHAPS YOU SHOULD STICK TO USING YOUR RIGHT HAND WHEN YOU GIVE ME A TRIM!

Anyway, the basic point is that by using extra senses, when doing daily activities, the mental wellbeing of your loved ones can be helped with little or no extra effort and no extra cost.

Identify a habit – and change that.

On the changing habit front, we aren't talking about smoking, although if you can encourage your loved one out of that habit you will certainly be doing something fantastic.

For promoting mental health though, a great form of brain exercise/fun that is easy, free and doable every day, is to break the habits of daily living.

This means perhaps changing the route driven or walked to the shops or to take a different bus to work or when visiting friends and family. Or even change the order that they water their plants in their garden, in their window boxes or around their house.

The trick is to look at all the activities that are performed in the same or similar manner every day or week and switch the order they are done in. When we are doing something familiar, seeing the same sights or doing the same actions, we automatically need to think less. Therefore, by placing ourselves in new situations with unfamiliar sights and sounds, we are giving our brain a great workout and increasing our brain reserves!

It hopefully now makes sense why brain exercises are so important for your ageing loved ones and how simple, cheap, effective and fun they can be.

It's important to remember that metal exercise and keeping a loved one mentally stimulated doesn't mean running them around all day. It simply means trying to raise people's awareness of what can happen to our minds as we age and giving them some basic tips that can make a real and significant impact on their mental wellbeing.

Important note:

Watching TV provides little or no mental stimulation, essentially sending our brain into a neutral state.

So for relaxation, TV can be great.

But as far as providing brain exercise, the only way a TV might be of benefit is if your ageing loved one dismantles the whole thing on their living room floor and puts it back together again.

Now, that would be a big-time brain workout!

For more information about brain exercises and contact details for some great brain activity products, please visit the Resources page on our website: **www.ActionForAgeing.com/Resources**

ACTION STEPS – Brain excercises/fun

1. Remind your ageing loved ones why brain exercises are beneficial. ☐

2. Remind your ageing loved ones that brain exercises are FUN. ☐

3. Activities and hobbies that require thought, analysis, reasoning and logic are all good for brain exercises. ☐

4. Memorising shopping lists is great for the brain. ☐

5. Using the odd hand to perform daily tasks is great for the brain. ☐

6. Specially designed computer games are great for the brain. ☐

7. Using as many senses as possible whilst performing daily tasks is great for the brain. ☐

8. Identifying and changing habits, like walking different routes to the shops, is great for the brain. ☐

9. Watching TV is not great for the brain. Building a TV definitely is though! ☐

TOPIC 9

Calendar

Fact: A custom-made photo calendar costs about £12.

Fact: If you make it BIG, it's harder to lose.

Make it a LARGE one. In the kitchen.

It's easy for people of all ages to lose track of appointments and engagements in the days, weeks and months ahead.

As we become older this is especially the case, as increased forgetfulness is one of the many shared challenges that unites us all.

One very helpful action that you might suggest is to have a large wall calendar in your loved one's kitchen so that there's a central place to record all their social engagements and appointments.

Carer Min

Over the years I have observed that medical appointment cards are commonly placed under a magnet and attached to the fridge.

I have also been in attendance when an appointment card has gone missing, resulting in a slightly heated exchange between family members.

"Mum. Your doctor's appointment was right there a few days ago, where have you put it?"

"I can't remember. Maybe it fell off and is under the fridge."

"I've already looked under the fridge. Do you know how long it's going to take me to ring the hospital and then track down when your appointment is?"

Phoning the hospital and working your way through the telephone system could waste an hour or so of your time.

My suggestion is a simple one. By all means store the appointment card on the fridge. However, as a permanent form of backup, a calendar could prove to be a valuable addition.

All appointments are recorded in one place. Perfect, unless the calendar goes missing!

There's no shortage of calendars available in stores across the land, so whether it is photos of butterflies, the Women's Institute getting saucy, or piglets in painted pots that your loved one wants to see every month, there is certainly something for everyone.

Also, many photo printing stores on your high street will print a customised calendar. Why not take in photos of grandchildren or favourite pets and have a custom made calendar for your loved one.

A lovely thought and something that will provide pleasure throughout the whole year.

If you would like to see our specialised Action for Ageing range of calendars, with extra large font and other practical enhancements, then please visit our website: **www.ActionForAgeing.com/Resources**

ACTION STEPS – Calendar

1. Design a large customised calendar for your loved one. ☐

2. Have a calendar printed at your local photo shop. Also makes a great gift! ☐

3. Encourage your loved one not to put it in the back of the hallway cupboard 'for safe keeping'. ☐

4. Suggest the calendar is kept in a central location. And used! ☐

Care planning

> Care planning is about taking positive and proactive steps to help maintain or improve your ageing loved one's wellbeing.
>
> It should not be seen as a dreadful Plan B alternative to living 100% independently.

Care planning is not usually something anyone thinks about until their ageing loved one experiences some sort of illness, accident or incident that not only highlights that they have become more vulnerable, but that they may also no longer be 100% independent and safe.

It is often a very difficult subject to have to address and therefore needs to be approached with great care and sensitivity. Keep in mind though, that discussing care options with your loved one might actually be welcomed by them, as it means relief from doing everything themselves. And, once they start to receive help or care in their home or if they move into a new care-based living environment, a care plan can improve their overall wellbeing.

When talking about care planning and care options, it's worth looking at what factors need to be considered when deciding on a care option and the different types of care that are available. Specifically, what they offer, what costs are involved and what funding options are available.

> ### Carer Min
>
> *Knowing that her ageing father, diagnosed with Alzheimer's, could no longer live by himself in his own home, a client's daughter arranged to have a studio unit built at the back of her home. Her father has settled in well and his two dogs are his beloved companions. Because the daughter has to work full time, she arranged for a service provider to attend three times daily for meal preparation, medication, and personal care. A happy resolution. The bonus is that the teenage grandchildren also honour their grandfather and provide lots of loving attention.*

The area of care planning is broad and complicated and the regulations, governing bodies, standard practises and terminology (amongst other things), change continuously.

The content we provide in this book and on our website is for summary information purposes only. It is not to be taken as advice. People should seek the latest information from a variety of sources (such as GPs, charities and reputable care planning services) before making any care planning assessments and decisions.

The below is only a very brief summary of what is involved. If you type in 'care planning' in the search box on our website, you will find much more detailed information. **www.ActionForAgeing.com**

So what are some of the things to consider when discussing Care and Care planning?

Personal factors

Does your loved one need help with:

- **food and drinks** – buying food, preparing and eating meals, maintaining a regular and healthy diet

- **shopping** – preparing a shopping list, doing the shopping at their local shops or online, arranging to have their shopping delivered

- **washing and hygiene** – having a regular bath or shower, brushing teeth, cutting nails

- **medical requirements** – taking medication, dressing any minor injuries, keeping themselves free of infection, able to raise an alarm in medical emergency

- **toiletry requirements** – needing assistance to use the toilet or help with alternatives such as incontinence pads or their colostomy bag

- **safety requirements** – maintaining a safe environment, not leaving oven or heaters on unintentionally, or forgetting to turn the hotplate or gas cooker flames off, not forgetting to close and lock their doors and windows, not inviting people they don't know into their home

- **dressing** – needing assistance to get dressed

- **household duties** – vacuuming or washing floors, washing dishes, doing the laundry, cleaning the bathroom, keeping the house in general safe and hygienic order

Your loved one's circumstances

- do they live by themselves?
- will they accept having a carer visit them or move in if necessary?
- can their home be modified to be made safer?

- are they vulnerable or at risk in the current living arrangements?
- how is their mobility?
- how are their communication skills?
- how is their mental health?
- do they or you have the funds available to have home modifications done?
- is there money to pay for a carer?
- is funding available from the government or charities to help pay for a carer to visit or perhaps even live-in?
- can family or friends share any or all of the carer duties (and is that okay with your loved one?)
- is a reputable carer service available in their area?
- how often is a carer needed each day or week?
- does the carer need any special skills?

Having identified what the care needs of an ageing loved one are or might soon be, it is then a case of looking at the various care options available.

These are generally made up of:

- homeshare
- home (domiciliary) care
- residential care
  - sheltered home/hostel
  - care home
  - care home with full services / nursing home

Homeshare

The Homeshare arrangement is where free or discounted accommodation in an older person's home is exchanged for the tenant performing home help activities. The type, level and frequency of help provided by the younger Homesharer will vary between individual requirements and arrangements agreed. Usually the Homesharer will do their regular job during the day and be required to be sleep overnight at least five or six nights a week and stay for a minimum fixed period, such as six months.

Benefits to your loved one:

- can maintain independence and live in their home for longer
- is cheaper than paying for a professional live-in Carer
- added security in having someone home with them overnight
- companionship
- some get help with household tasks like cooking, cleaning and shopping
- as well as personal care such as dressing and washing in mornings and evenings

Benefits to the Homesharer:

- receive low cost accommodation
- might get to learn a bit more about life from the experiences, adventures and misadventures of the older person!
- satisfaction from helping someone who really needs it
- contributes to living an interesting life
- forging new friendships and relationships with families

If you wish to find out more about Homeshare, and contact details of a program in your area, please visit the website of the charity Homeshare International. **www.homeshare.org**

Home (Domiciliary) Care

Having a Carer visit your loved one's home weekly, daily, remain all day or actually live in 24-hours a day.

This option enables your loved one to stay in their home, having someone who is trained visiting them regularly and where the duties of the Carer can be specified. These can be to assist in dressing or washing or meal preparation. Or household cleaning, medication monitoring or simply accompanying your loved one on a trip to their local shops.

Carer Min

Some years ago I met a wonderful ageing couple who wished to remain living in their own home.

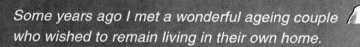

Happily married for 64 years. Their six offspring decided to all contribute to arranging for a live-in carer, who would be regularly relieved by other carers. This was truly a 'win-win' solution because the parents were able to continue living their normal lives, the family enjoyed peace of mind, and the full time carer (me) did not become over-fatigued. A great example of people all working together.

It is often the most desired option because retaining a sense of independence by living in their home is one of the key contributors to wellbeing amongst older people. Home care also provides a high degree of flexibility around the level and type of care received.

The costs obviously depend on what care is received. Your loved one may qualify for funding assistance, depending on their financial circumstances. Government policy may be that the user (your loved one) should pay for their own care until they only have assets left below a certain value or until they have paid for themselves up to a certain amount. The rules change regularly, so please visit our website and look under the 'Care planning' section for information on current funding or assistance options.

For information on who to contact with respect to professional carers and care service providers, please visit the Resources section on our website: **www.ActionForAgeing.com/resources**

Residential Care

Sometimes remaining living in their own home or moving in with a relative or a friend is not the best option for an older person, for any variety of reasons. The alternative then, is Residential Care.

It's important to note that moving into residential care should not be seen as only a negative option, because these days there is a very wide variety of residential care types available. This means that whilst there may be a natural reluctance to consider residential living, once people find out the variety of services and lifestyle options available, then it may feel like a positive move.

The benefits such as the increased social life and social activity opportunities, the reduction of stress related to managing and maintaining their home and having closer medical attention can help contribute towards maintaining or even increasing new resident's well-being.

WELCOME TO SUNNY HILLS, MR SMITH I'M JUDY FROM No 23... AND SINGLE.

It might be that a couple move into a form of residential care together or that if one of the partners is suffering from something like dementia, that the best (albeit reluctant) option is for one of your loved ones to move into residential care by themselves.

Also, the variety of services offered within the different residential care settings is huge and growing, as awareness of and demand for different services increases.

The scenarios and situations differ from family to family, which is why it's helpful for everyone to be aware of care and care planning and the possible alternatives.

As for residential care, this is a term that covers all sorts of living arrangements and the 'official' names vary depending on who you speak to and the terminology of different stakeholders.

The three main types of Residential care are:

- Shelter/hostel
- Care homes
- Nursing homes

Sheltered Home / Hostel

These are where your loved one can live independently within an older people's community, either in their own flat within a building or in a bungalow within the grounds. People retain their independence as they largely look after themselves, and benefit from having a manager close by to assist and from living in a (usually) active older people's community. Also, the flats/bungalows are built especially to promote safer living with kitchens, bedrooms, bathrooms and household fittings all modified for older people's needs.

They may also have a shop, restaurant and laundrette on site as well as medical and security services.

If your loved one does require regular carer assistance, they can be arranged in the same way as if they were employed for Home care.

Where people require more direct care and assisted living, then the next alternative is moving into a care home.

Care Home

If your loved one is no longer able to live comfortably and safely by themselves or with their partner, then perhaps a care home is more suitable. These are usually purpose-built facilities that provide residents with a private bedroom and bathroom and all their basic living requirements, such as meals, laundry and cleaning. The residents don't have to worry about paying household bills and they benefit from increased security, the availability of immediate help 24/7, basic nursing services and regular social activities organised onsite and offsite. The residents in a care home may have a variety of mobility issues yet are still able to maintain a reasonable degree of independence and management of their personal daily activities.

Carer Min

I spent two years working in an older people's hostel, often working shifts in their special facility, where the dementia residents were cared for.

In the storeroom of the special care facility was an icecream container full of dentures, that had accumulated over a long period of time.

As a denture was discoverd somewhere within the facility, for example, hidden in amongst the jigsaw puzzle drawer, the staff on duty would do the rounds and endeavour to locate the owner. If this didn't happen, after day or two, the denture would join the others in the icecream container.

The level of medical support and variety of care services for residents can vary considerably between care homes as can the atmosphere, the quality of facilities and services, the variety of activities and the experience and attitude of the staff. This is why it is important for people to seek advice on care home planning and selection, from a reputable advice service. The advice service will be able to guide your family through the process of assessing your loved one's needs and then help identify the most suitable care homes based on price, location, living and medical requirements, and a multitude of other factors that you will definitely want to consider. For those whose needs surpass what can be provided in a care home environment, the nursing home is the next alternative.

Nursing Home

Where your loved one requires more intensive care and medical attention than is available in a standard or even advanced care home environment, the next option for them is to move into a nursing home.

Nursing homes provide additional specialised equipment and services to cater for residents who are a considerable way along the care path and requiring more intensive day-to-day support to deal with the challenges of advanced ageing.

Residents in a nursing home are people who require 24/7 hour nursing care, assistance and rehabilitative services. Some residents might only be temporary, because they are recovering from an accident such as a fall, whilst others may only be in for a few days as part of respite for their carer/family who need a break.

The type of facilities, environment and staff will vary from one home to another, so it is important for people to do as much research as possible to help locate the most suitable place for their loved one.

Sometimes residents may need to supply their own equipment. For example, if it is specialised, not included as part of their care package or it is not required to be provided by the facility.

Whilst many homes are privately owned, they are inspected regularly and must meet the National Care Standards that are set by NICE (National Institute for Health and Clinical Excellence).

Care planning is a very important activity that you and your loved ones may need to address at some point along the track. When introducing the topic of care and wanting to discuss care options, it is important to approach it with great sensitivity as the further loss of independence and coping with a change in living can be very difficult and traumatic for your ageing loved one and the rest of the family. Where possible, it helps to focus on the benefits of the new environment and how the wellbeing of your loved one can be improved. One of the biggest factors that impacts choice of care is money (no surprise there!), so like everything, the sooner people can start preparing financially for their care needs with things like a care savings plan or other investment, the better off everyone will be.

By having adequate savings or funds for care, people are able to help themselves avoid situations in later life where, for example, a person is required to move out of the care home or nursing home that they have been enjoying living in, because they have run out of adequate funds. The exact care funding rules and options depend on the policy of the government of the day.

In short, as with all topics and actions for ageing, the sooner you are aware of what may lay ahead and start actively planning for them, the better off you and your loved ones will be.

If you wish to find out more about Homeshare, and contact details of a program in your area, please visit the website of the charity Homeshare International. **www.homeshare.org**

For more detailed information on care planning, the latest funding options and contact details for reputable care advisors, please visit the Resources page of our website: **www.ActionForAgeing.com/ Resources**

ACTION STEPS – Care planning

1. Research the information provided on care and the potential options available. ☐

2. Then share this information and website links with family and friends. ☐

3. Encourage discussion with your ageing loved ones about their preferences for care provision and the possible alternatives. ☐

4. Encourage everyone to keep an open mind about when to seek help and in what form. ☐

5. Sometimes a person receiving a little bit of help at home may enable them to keep living independently for longer, than if they try to manage by themselves but with increasing difficulty. ☐

6. There are many factors to consider and a wide variety of services available, so people can definitely benefit from receiving independent advice from a professional care advisor. ☐

Carer's resources

> **Fact:** There are six million unpaid carers in the UK.
>
> **Fact:** Seventeen per cent of all people aged 45-64 are actively caring – giving help or special care to someone.
>
> **Fact:** Eighty-three per cent of those aged 45-54 are worse off as a result of caring.

By now, you will hopefully be more aware of what it means to be a Carer, what some of the negative impacts of ageing can be and what life might be like if you are called upon by a loved one for ongoing, sustained support.

It can be a very difficult and challenging experience, but one that can be greatly helped if information and help is sought from the various specialist services available.

Given the speed of change and development currently occurring in the world of care for older people, it is best if you refer to our Resources page on our website, for the latest and most comprehensive listing of resources.

You may not be a carer today, but it is likely that at some point in the next few years you will be called upon to provide support to your loved one in some way.

The earlier you seek out information and apply the actions suggested in books such as this, the better, healthier and ultimately happier you and your loved one's lives will be.

ACTION STEPS – Carer's resources

1.   Go to **www.ActionForAgeing.com/Resources**

TOPIC 12

Clothing

Fact: For the under 50s clothing and footwear as a % of total household expenditure = 6% = £27 per week.

Fact: For the over 65s it = 4% = £7 per week.

APPARENTLY MY TROUSERS ARE FASHIONABLE LIKE THIS!

Comfort is king

Some people are not particularly fussed about clothing style and approach what they wear in mostly functional terms. Is it comfortable and suitable for the weather or activity of the day, does it look clean and tidy and is it at a price they are happy to pay?

Whilst other people may be very interested in fashion and being stylishly dressed, and would regard their appearance as being a key component of their sense of wellbeing. Then there are other people who are somewhere in the middle, or at the extreme on either side.

As we are all different in our attitude towards clothing, the longer people can be responsible for their own clothing selection, the better. Where ageing or injury has had an effect on mobility or people's ability to dress themselves, the comfort of clothing and ease of dressing becomes increasingly important.

Carer Min

The key attribute when clothes shopping for a person with an injury or restricted flexibility, is loose.

Buttons should be avoided or kept to a minimum (and at the front, not the back of the garment).

A tip when assisting someone in dressing who has a bad arm or leg, always place the clothing over the bad limb first and then follow on with the second limb. This helps avoid unnecessary discomfort.

Also, try to avoid clothing that has a belt, fiddly flaps and buttons or lots of pockets. As people become more forgetful, the fewer places on their person that they can lose things in, the better.

Traditionally, women love clothes and even while young they tend to have full wardrobes, so, without realising it they begin a lifetime habit of hoarding.

As I have travelled around, I have encountered some amazing wardrobes. Wardrobes bulging with garments jammed on hangers and then the area above and underneath the hung items are also absolutely stuffed with more piles of clothes.

So many times I have seen plastic supermarket bags crammed full with more clothing and then stacked high along the walls.

One lady I met had run out of room in her wardrobe and across her floor, so had moved further bags onto her bed.

> *We all know that even in a million years most of these clothes will never be worn; the majority don't even fit any more.*
>
> *So, I would definitely encourage a regular clothes clear out from as early as possible, to prevent any hoarding habits from starting or to break any hoarding habits that have already begun.*

Clothes hoarding

Once the hoarding fixation has really set in, it can be very difficult and stressful to get your loved one to part with even the most redundant of clothing items.

Having clothes stacked up everywhere throughout your loved one's house, will not only look messy and possibily terrify the grandkids, but more importantly it can make living in their home much more dangerous.

Having to navigate through bags everywhere represents a huge and frequently realised risk to your loved one, who can trip and fall over something that is sticking out or has fallen onto the floor.

And falling clothes are not like a falling stack of crockery. Clothes can topple over and not make a sound, so if your loved one has knocked something over, they may not notice it across their path until they are halfway through their fall.

By that time, it's a bit late for all concerned.

You might be surprised at how widespread and common the clothes hoarding habit really is.

Additional point:

If you buy clothing for someone with restricted flexibility that is easy to put on and take off, you are helping preserve their independence. People being able to dress themselves is a key element in retaining their independence.

If you would like to find out about some specialist clothes shops for older people who have difficulty dressing, please visit the Resources page on our website: **www.ActionForAgeing.com/ Resources**

ACTION STEPS – Clothing

1. Encourage people to make their own clothing choices for as long as possible. ☐

2. When it comes to clothing for people who have difficulty dressing, look for loose and comfortable. ☐

3. Front buttoning is preferable to back buttoning, unless your loved one is bed or chair bound, where back buttons are best. ☐

4. Avoid where possible the need for belts, unnecessary fiddly buttons and garments with too many pockets. ☐

5. Every additional pocket is somewhere else for the keys to hide. ☐

6. Nip clothes hoarding in the bud. Get clothes cleared out regularly from early on. Otherwise it can be a huge source of stress and risk later. ☐

7. Avoid clothes with zippers. ☐

8. Choose clothes with natural fibres that breathe, like cotton. ☐

9. Choose clothes that can be frequently washed in hot water. ☐

10. Choose clothes with elastic waists. ☐

11. Choose tops that open at the back for bed bound people. ☐

12. Providing clothing with easy access helps to maintain your loved one's sense of independence. ☐

13. Introduce garments with velco where possible – especially to replace fiddly buttons that can be difficult and painful for loved ones with stiff finger joints. ☐

14. Purchase dressing devices such as dressing sticks for helping to hook garments over shoulders, socks or tight aids, long handled shoehorns and other simple products that can be enormously helpful in minimising the bending, reaching and twisting that dressing usually involves. ☐

Commode chair

> **Fact:** Commode chairs start from a cost of approximately £60.
>
> **Fact:** They come in more varieties than most would imagine.

A shorter hop for when nature calls

If your loved one is not making it to the toilet in time, or if they encounter difficulty mobilising when nature calls, a commode chair in the bedroom or living area can help solve the problem.

Commode chairs are essentially a regular chair, with a toilet seat and bucket in the middle. Some look as that sounds, while others look like a regular chair.

They aren't a piece of furniture we talk about or hear much about. Until you need one. If you are not as agile as you once were, having a portable toilet available nearby your bed, or elsewhere in the house, can be very helpful indeed.

Also, rushing for a toileting emergency is one of the most common causes of older people having a fall. The more that can be avoided, the better.

Variety of styles:

These days, commode chairs come in all shapes, sizes and styles.

- You can get very discreet ones, with a seat cover that when down, makes the commode look like a regular, stylish living room chair.

- You can also get very basic dining chair styles that are very light and portable or wheelchair type commodes that can be wheeled into a shower.

- If there is no one to help your loved one to empty their commode, then a chemical toilet might be more appropriate.

- Where mobility is limited but still at a reasonable level, rather than a commode your loved one may consider having a toilet installed in a convenient location, near their living area for daytime use.

- If toileting looks like it will be or already is an issue, contact your GP or occupational therapist to assess your loved one's needs and their home to help determine what type of toileting solution is the most suitable.

Carer Min

When transporting the waste container I'd recommend wearing vinyl gloves to avoid any cross infection.

And if you have nipped in the bud any clothes hoarding habits, then hopefully that will reduce your risk of tripping over!! That's another good reason to get those unused clothes down to the charity shop.

Remember:

Many of the topics we discuss may seem extreme and irrelevant now, but it's good to read about them anyway because they may well be part of your reality tomorrow.

Also please remember:

Given the personal nature of the topic, it is very important that people approach it in as sensitive a way as possible. One of the reasons incontinence is such a problem is because people are reluctant to talk about it, even with their closest family or friends. So if you can raise it in a gentle way with your ageing loved one to help avoid embarrassment, that is a very special and kind action.

If you want to find out more about health care professionals who can assess what toileting equipment solution best suits your loved one's needs, see the Resources page on our website: **www.ActionForAgeing.com/Resources**

If you want to locate suppliers of commode chairs and other toileting products, please visit our website Resources page at:**www.ActionForAgeing.com/Resources**

ACTION STEPS – Commode chair

1. Be aware of what types of commode chairs are available, as the wide variety may be surprising. ☐

2. Suggest your loved one receives advice from their GP or a health care professional. ☐

3. Discuss these issues with your loved one now, even if they don't currently need toileting equipment. The more used to it we are now, the better prepared we will be if the issue does become a reality for our loved ones and family along the tracks. ☐

TOPIC 14

Dignity

> **Critical topic:** Helping ageing loved ones maintain their dignity is very, very important!

Dignity refers to how considerately people feel they are being treated and the worth that people feel is being placed upon them. For today's younger generations, who might have a more self-focused approach to how they interact with others, being concerned about showing and receiving respect in the traditional sense (politeness, deference and displaying good manners) may seem quaint and of little importance.

So why does Dignity get its own Topic?

Because, dignity is one of the most important factors contributing towards a person's wellbeing. As Carers (which is what you, your family and friends will possibly be one day in one form or another) we need to remember that our loved one's dignity needs to be respected, protected and maintained at all times.

This may seem very obvious to some, however it is very easy for this to slip off our radar when we are busy trying to juggle 100 things in our life. What may be intended as a practical or simple solution to us may not take into full consideration the impact it may have on the sense of dignity of your ageing loved one. This awareness and respect of dignity also extends to how older people feel they are being treated in public.

A very simple example is where an older person gets onto a crowded train or bus. In times gone by, there would be no question about younger people getting up to offer the older person their seat. If they didn't, then the older person may well have given them a clip around the ear with a newspaper and told them to get up.

Fast forward to today and when an older person gets on crowded public transport the availability of a seat is not automatic and if they ask a younger person for their seat, the response will most likely be varied. If the older person gives the younger person a whack with their newspaper, they will probably be arrested for assault or infringing on the younger person's human rights. Of course this is a wild generalisation and it is not the case that the world today is full of heartless, young people. Far from it. But the point is simply that the world has changed, our values and behaviours have changed and that the awareness and approach to dignity and what it means sometimes seems considerably different between the younger and older generations.

Regarding dignity and how we care for our ageing loved ones, studies have identified eight primary contributing factors that contribute to an older person's sense of independence and provide the basis for their overall wellbeing.

1. **Control and choice:** People feeling like they are in control of the choices being made regarding what they do, where they live and how they are cared for.

   Good: "Maybe it's time we looked at the pros and cons of alternative living arrangements?"

   Bad: "Pack your bags. You're off to the nursing home."

2. **Practical help:** People managing to live independently with a small amount of help.

   Good: "Yes, I can come over and change the light bulb in the living room for you."

Bad: "No. If you can't scoot up a ladder and change your own light bulb, then it's off to the care home for you. Pack your bags! Yes, in the dark if necessary."

3. **Social inclusion:** People need to feel that they are connected to other people, be they family, friends, people in their neighbourhood or with people who share an interest. Isolation and loneliness are unfortunately quite common problems for older people.

Good: "We will pick you up at 10am, as the circus starts at midday."

Bad: "Sorry, we have to cancel today's visit too. Little Johnny has a sore stomach from eating all his Easter eggs. We will come and visit you at Christmas though. I promise."

4. **Communication:** People having a sense that their view is being listened to and is respected.

Good: "You're right. I'll call someone who is qualified to install your new gas boiler."

Bad: "Nah, I can install your boiler. Why pay someone a grand to connect a couple of pipes?"

5. **Privacy:** People need to feel that their personal information, their personal space and the provision of their personal care, is being respected and remaining confidential.

Good: "Here are your tablets, Mr Jones."

Bad: "Here are your tablets, Mr Jones. My wife was wondering if there was an interesting story behind how you caught pneumonia in the first place?"

6. **Nutrition and eating:** People having a variety and choice of tasty meals and support in eating it where possible.

   Good: "Would you like a fresh salad or roast winter vegetables with your lasagne?"

   Bad: "This week, it's fish fingers. Next week it's chips."

7. **Personal hygiene:** People receiving help to maintain their regular standards of hygiene.

   Good: "If we soak your toe-nails in warm water, they will be easier to cut."

   Bad: "I'd probably need a hack-saw to get through those nails. Let's wait for the podiatrist to do it. He's due back next April."

8. **Pain management:** People having the right services provided and the right type and level of medication to help with their pain, so that their wellbeing is being maintained or improved.

   Good: "It's great to hear the change to the capsules has helped ease your indigestion."

   Bad: "When things get really painful, take this block of wood and bite on it."

> **Please note:** The above examples are intentionally extreme. Dignity can be impacted in many subtle ways. The more thought and consideration we can show to people, the better!

Many people of the older generations have valued and maintained their sense of dignity throughout their lives by how they have treated others and how they have expected others to treat them. So when it comes to their sense of personal wellbeing in later life, a critical part of that is the respect that is provided to them by those who are caring for them in some capacity. Their wellbeing is also impacted by how they feel they are respected and treated by their community too and in having a sense of belonging or inclusion. Even a simple chat at the bus stop with a stranger, can make a significant difference to a person's day.

For more information on ways to help people maintain their independence, their sense of dignity and help with their overall wellbeing, please... consider putting into action some of the hundreds of tips in the book AND hopefully suggesting that your friends and family might do the same too!

ACTION STEPS – For helping maintain dignity and wellbeing

1. Try to ensure that your loved one feels they have choices and control over their decisions. ☐

2. Check where practical help around the home can be provided to promote continued independence and wellbeing. ☐

3. Where possible, include your ageing loved ones in plans and encourage them to remain socially active. ☐

4. Try to maintain good communication and respect each other's opinions. ☐

5. It's important to respect people's private information and their personal space. ☐

6. Try to ensure your loved ones continue to enjoy a choice and variety of tasty and nutritious meals and if they need assistance in preparing or eating, that it is being received. ☐

7. Keep an eye out for your ageing loved one's hygiene and with as much sensitivity as possible, offer help or suggestions if you feel that they are maybe no longer maintaining it successfully by themselves. ☐

8. Encourage your loved one to seek regular advice about their pain and medication management from their doctor. Sometimes by changing the frequency and type of medication they are on, or services that are being provided, people can improve their personal wellbeing. ☐

9. A great starting position is for people to treat others as they wish to be treated themselves. ☐

TOPIC 15

Driving

Fact: The fatality rate for drivers aged 85 and over is nine times as high as the rate for drivers aged 18-67.

Extra care required

In the UK, there are currently 9.5 million drivers who are 65 years old, and that number is estimated to balloon to 13 million within ten years.

The fatality rate for drivers aged 85 and over is nine times as high as the rate of drivers aged between 18 and 67.

What we need to do is:

- Raise awareness to the dangers of driving as we get older.
- Encourage honest, frequent, competency self-assessment.

Driving is often linked with independence and independence is an important part of wellbeing. Also, sometimes people's loved ones might be in denial of their inability to drive. For all these reasons, the family doctor or a member of the family needs to approach the subject with great tact and empathy.

Carer Min

The son of a client removed the car battery from his father's car because he was so concerned that his father could be involved in an accident himself, with the possibility of injuring others.

His father knew that his car was immobilised, but couldn't work out why. He simply commented to everyone who visited, "I must get the car looked at." However, he didn't pursue the matter.

When the time to stop driving arrives, people can encounter a kind of grief because they feel as if they are giving up their independence.

When this difficult decision is required, people can become distressed and withdraw into themselves.

When a teenager gets their driving licence and the set of keys to their first car, they are excited about the new world of opportunities opening up before them.

Similarly, when an older person has to hand their keys over and sell their car, they do so feeling that their world of opportunities might now be diminishing.

Carer Min

One lady I knew was a somewhat erratic driver. Whilst reversing into her carport she simply kept right on going, out of the back of the carport, across her lawn, through the back fence and ended up in the garden of the people living behind.

She had never met them before. She did then. And decided it was time to stop driving.

I used to visit an older gentleman who drove his car to the newsagents to purchase his paper every day.

He knew he was home when he felt the car hit the letter box. The front and side of the car was a vision to behold.

One side of the car looked as though it was being beaten to death, the other side was perfect. This gentleman only drove to the newsagents daily because he had no memory of how to drive anywhere else. Time to stop driving.

Driving mishaps occur within any age group. However, there is a time for all of us to set down the car keys for the last time.

The car isn't the only way to get around. Electric scooters and other motorised trolleys are a wonderful way for older people to stay on the move. Of course, to ensure that your loved one is competent and to find out what sort of scooter is recommended, their doctor should be consulted first.

> ## Carer Min
>
> *I had a terrific client, Dennis, who set out regularly to scoot up to the local shopping centre. The scooter's battery lasted seventeen kilometres and Dennis was perfectly aware of this fact.*
>
> *One day he set off and became side tracked when he decided to go and have a look at the shops in the next suburb. He was half way home and it was pouring with rain, when suddenly his battery went flat.*
>
> *What a performance it was to assist Dennis as well as the motorised trolley (which required a small truck!) to return home. Promising to head no further than the local shops, Dennis was never caught short again.*

Loved one's should be encouraged to remain as active and independent for as long as possible.

To help them do so safely:

- apply for a blue badge for their windscreen to make parking easier and more convenient
- encourage regular eyesight checks
- help them to keep driving, if they are competent
- help them to stop driving, if they're not

If you would like additional information about blue badge applications, electric scooters or charities that can help advise you on how to resolve your concerns about an ageing loved one's driving, please visit the Resources page on our website: **www.ActionForAgeing.Com/resources**

ACTION STEPS – Driving

1. Monitor your loved one's driving. ☐

2. Look out for new bumps and scrapes on their car. ☐

3. Raise your loved one's awareness that they need to be careful. ☐

4. Encourage honest and frequent competency assessment. ☐

5. Check if an electric mobility vehicle might be safer than a car. ☐

6. Perhaps seek information on whether your loved one is eligible for a Blue Badge application? Links to the relevant contacts can be found on our website Resources page. ☐

7. If you feel your loved one might not be able to drive competently, for their own safety and that of other road users, it is best to bring the subject up quickly. ☐

8. As it can have such a significant impact on your loved one, it's important to approach the subject with great sensitivity. ☐

9. Perhaps seek the advice of and enlist the help of their GP. ☐

Empathy

> **Fact:** Depression is more common amongst the over-65s than in any other age group.
>
> **Fact:** Depression affects 20% of the over-65s living in the community.
>
> **Fact:** Depression affects 40% of the over-65s living in a care home.

Realise that your loved one is changing

We get so used to running around doing everything at full speed with maximum efficiency in our little life bubbles, that by the time we reach middle age, we have forgotten that not everyone of every age operates at the same level.

A good exercise is to stop and look at the world though your ageing loved one's eyes, to think about what makes them tick, what their interests are, what their fears are and how:

1. You can best help them.
2. You can best help them help themselves.

If your ageing loved one is healthy and safe and happy, then that has a very positive impact on your and your loved one's life.

It is somewhat inevitable though, that your loved ones will have age-related challenges and the more sensitive you and your family can be to the changes, the better their wellbeing will be helped.

Changes that can have a negative impact on your loved one's wellbeing and that are linked to illnesses such as depression include:

- a loss of independence due to decreased mobility
- chronic pain caused by possibly multiple medical conditions
- moving to a new home or care facility
- isolation and loneliness
- struggles with memory loss and mental deterioration
- financial concerns about how their future care will be funded

And these are but a few.

Carer Min

During my twenties, thirties and forties, when I encountered older people, mainly relatives, I used to become exasperated because they seemingly took forever to do anything. Eating a meal. Getting into the car. Getting dressed. Going to the bathroom.

I'd be all organised, ready to go and they would simply ignore my muttered, "Come on, we have to leave right now!" pleadings.

When I moved into my caring career I tried the same tactics with my clients and I encountered no more success than I'd had with my relatives. Someone was going to have to change and it certainly wasn't going to be them!

What I have learned is to appreciate how the world is through the older person's eyes and to adjust my behavior and expectations where necessary, so that their wellbeing remains the number one priority.

Carer Min

Throughout my caring years I have developed tremendous respect for older people, mainly for their ability to stand strong in the face of adversity.

- *death of a dearly loved partner or child, family and friends*
- *loss of mobility*
- *lack of finances*
- *loss of independence – e.g. no longer being able to drive*
- *loss of hearing, eyesight*
- *coping with side effects from being in WW2, or other war and conflict situations*
- *variety of physical ailments requiring medication and hospital visits*

I have learnt so much from my clients. Patience, tolerance, humour and frankness.

In my mind, to show empathy, I need to imagine what it must be like to be living in my client's shoes and act accordingly with kindness.

Inevitably what I have found, in working with older people, is that they have taught me to be a far nicer person, who is happy to enjoy their company and can appreciate my own blessings more.

I think this is a real benefit which most carers would agree has been a side effect of their time as a carer.

Remember that whilst this Topic and its action steps relate to people currently in the caring role, it is of equal importance to those people who are not currently caring for a loved one but will be in the years ahead.

The sooner people can receive the information in this book and take action to proactively improve the health, safety and happiness of their loved ones, the better off their life and that of their loved ones will be.

Prevention is better than cure.

For information on Depression amongst older people, its causes, symptoms and potential treatments, please seek the advice of your ageing loved one's GP. There are also charities and groups set up to provide support and resources for people and their families who are struggling to cope with Depression. Please visit our website Resources page for more information and contact details. **www.ActionForAgeing.com**

ACTION STEPS – Empathy

1. Remember to appreciate that your loved one is not as young or mobile as they once were. ☐

2. Remember to appreciate that many ageing loved ones have had to endure many hardships and are still climbing a tough mountain with new challenges, every day. ☐

3. Our loved ones can bring out the best, and worst, in us. So lets try and fix the worst and enjoy the best. ☐

4. Shocking thought: You will be regarded as an 'older person' some day too. How do you hope you will be treated? ☐

TOPIC 17

Falls

FALL PREVENTION
is
ABSOLUTELY
(one of)
the
MOST IMPORTANT
topics
in this book.

And the most critical tip for you to action.

Carer Min

I am penning these words whilst holidaying with my family. Family members wander by and enquire, "How's the writing going?" They also enquire as to my wellbeing.

A particular reason for their concern is that on the first day here, I fell. I was walking across the lounge room of the holiday rental and totally forgot there was a single step down into the dining room level. Being unable to 'walk on air' I landed on the stone tiles with an unbecoming thud. Luckily for me I fell on to my left side hip. If it had been my right side, which had already been weakened by a previous fall, I might well have broken a limb.

For someone who regards herself as being extremely conscious of the dangers of falling by older people, as well as myself (at a sprightly sixty-one years of age), it was a wake-up call.

Amongst the over 65s, every year:

Fact: Falls are the leading cause of injury-death.

Fact: Falls are also the primary reason for trauma based hospital admission and the most frequent cause of non-fatal injury.

Fact: There are 3.4 million reported falls.

Fact: And over 10 million unreported falls.

Fact: 13.4 million falls = 36,700 people falling every day!!

Fact: One in three falls are preventable. That's over 10,000 a day!!

Fact: We all have to get prevention awareness raised!!

Prevention is better than cure

Fall prevention is absolutely the single most critical topic in this book.

So critical in fact, it's worth repeating.

Fall prevention is absolutely the single most critical topic in this book.

Please get a highlighter pen now so that you can highlight the key information, tips and action steps in the following pages.

Scenario 1

Having a shower like any other day ➡ slip ➡ grab at shower door handle ➡ fall over ➡ injure hip ➡ call ambulance ➡ go to hospital A&E ➡ hip fractured ➡ hospitalised for 4 weeks ➡ 1 month later, go home and spend 3 weeks of 22 hours-a-day in bed, taking large doses of pain killers ➡ 2 months after fall, have limited mobility ➡ specialist recommends a hip replacement ➡ on NHS waiting list for hip replacement operation ➡ wait 3 months for operation ➡ housebound in meantime, continue with 2 hours limited mobility per day and taking huge doses of pain killer ➡ go into hospital for hip replacement ➡ spend 2 weeks in hospital ➡ go home ➡ spend 3 months on physiotherapy ➡ get 80% of mobility back and lifetime of pain killing medication ➡ continue on with life.

Scenario 2

Having a shower like any other day ➡ slip ➡ grab hold of shower safety bar ➡ stop self from falling ➡ finish showering ➡ have cup of tea ➡ continue on with life.

It really is as simple a choice as that. Prevention is better than cure.

Falls are happening every day and causing serious injury and even death.

This is very bad.

But, by taking some simple, precautionary measures you can significantly help prevent or reduce the frequency of falls by your loved ones and keep them healthier and happier for longer.

This is very good.

> **Fact:** Of the 3.4 million known falls every year, it is estimated that one million of those are preventable!!

The sole purpose of this action is to raise your awareness of the risk of falling and try reduce a chunk of those one million falls that are preventable.

When we're talking falls, it's probably handy to remind you of the different types of falls older people can have, by looking at what can actually cause a fall.

CAUSES OF FALLS

External causes

Firstly, there are endless external causes of a fall, so here's a few to get the ball rolling: soapy bathtub, wet kitchen floor, electrical cord from lamp, corner of coffee table, dog underfoot, cat's tail, frayed rug, old slipper, polished floor, poor lighting, jacket on ground, loose gravel, shoe in hallway, ice on pathway, hose in garden, worn stair carpet, broom head, oil on driveway, tea towel on floor or moss on decking.

To answer your question regarding the 'cat's tail', when an older person accidentally stands on their cat's tail, the cat lets out a blood-curdling scream, which frightens them and can cause them to jump, lose their balance and topple over.

It didn't mean that the cat's tail was so huge that they tripped over it, like a log. Although the way some people fatten their cats up with huge servings of food, some of their tails are probably log-like and a tripping risk in their own right.

Anyway, let's not digress.

Along with the numerous external influences that can lead to a fall, there are also many internal causes that lead to loved ones taking a tumble.

Internal causes

A few of those are: poor eyesight, loss of balance, loss of hand/eye co-ordination, lack of concentration, slowing of reflexes, failing memory, reduced strength, anxiety causing one to rush, lack of judgement, incontinence, medication, alcohol, low weight/body mass index, neurological problems (e.g. due to stroke) or a lack of confidence due to a previous fall.

Often it is a combination of external and internal factors that leads to older people landing on the floor and doing themselves a dreadful injury.

What's important for you to note, is that there are many, many potential causes behind a fall.

Hence, it's important to note what steps you and your loved ones can action, to help prevent the causes of a fall from happening, or at least help reduce their frequency or likelihood.

> ### Carer Min
>
> *I had a client whose life had changed dramatically as a result of a fall incurred when she had a heart attack. She fell and cut her foot badly. The foot became infected and her leg was amputated above the knee, and she now wears a prothesis. Her son resigned from his employment to care full time for his ageing mother, as well as his father who was suffering from Alzheimer's. The son presented as being in 'stress overload', his 'lifeline' being that carers attended daily.*

> There are many tips for fall prevention.
>
> Here is a selection of the most effective.

Fall prevention steps

It would be great if everyone could put a tick next to each on the whole list, but for a start, if you could select even just two that are suitable/achievable, then you are categorically helping your ageing loved ones towards having a healthier, hence happier, life.

It's not rocket science and just because you might be familiar with some or even all of them, that doesn't mean diddly squat unless you action them.

This isn't a test of what you have heard of, it's a list of things you should make a choice from and action at least one or two of them.

So here goes:

Internal prevention

Internal preventative measures: things your loved ones can do to/for their bodies, to help reduce the number or frequency of falls they experience.

Exercise

Specifically for balance, co-ordination and strength.

Performing ten minutes of simple balance and strengthening exercise per day, will help prevent your loved ones from having a fall. This is a repeated, verified, global study proven fact.

Exercise leads to a 50% reduction in falls.

Not 5% or 10% but a 50% reduction in falls, due to exercise.

Studies have also identified the shocking facts that:

Only 44% of older people are even aware that certain exercises can help prevent falls.

And

20% can't even remember the last time they did any exercise.

Crazy!!

We need to spread the message. Pronto.

If you can do it for your ageing loved one and family, that is fantastic, as raising awareness and changing people's mindset can only happen gradually over time.

There are basic **balance exercises** such as:

- Those used in tai-chi, where your loved one can step in and turn and step out, to improve balance.
- Hand/eye co-ordination via rubber ball throwing and catching.
- Steady and repeated dance movements for improved balance and concentration.

There's a series of simple **stretches**, where your loved one:

- Reaches slowly downwards with their hands towards their knees and back up.
- Raises their arms to the right and then left, helping maintain their agility and sense of balance.

Please note: when performing these types of stretches your loved one should be very careful not to rush or put themselves at risk of getting a rush of blood to the head and losing their balance.

For **strengthening**, your loved one can:

- Repeatedly raise themselves from a sitting to standing position.
- Perform resistance exercises against heavy/solid objects such as refrigerators, cars or walls.

Please note before embarking on an exercise program, your loved one must seek specific, personal advice from their doctor or a trained healthcare professional.

The tips in this book are supposed to raise your awareness of the important preventative role that exercise represents for your loved one.

> ### Carer Min
>
> *As a carer, one is introduced to many wonderful clients who have undergone difficult times. One such lovely lady fell and broke her pelvis, resulting in an extended hospital stay. Upon release she returned home and informed her ageing husband that she would spend the rest of her life living on the couch. When I met her, some weeks later, she was still on the couch refusing to attempt to try and walk with her walker. One day I tried a little bit of tough love and encouraged her to get to her feet in order to go to the shower. To my amazement she stood up and walked to the shower. Her husband was agog.*

Every older person needs specific advice from a professional about which exercises are most suitable for them.

And whilst any exercise is a benefit, the above help specifically with balance, strength and co-ordination. If your loved one goes for a walk every day, that is great for their body in general, but does not necessarily help them in their efforts towards fall prevention.

> **All sensible exercise is good.**
>
> **But specific fall-reduction exercises are critical.**

A wonderful side effect of people attending local exercise-related activities is that it encourages regular exercise (peer pressure) and it provides a basis for social interaction with other people. During the exercises, they can pick up advice and tips from their peers and share their experiences with the other group members. This then becomes an enjoyable weekly activity they can look forward to rather than a chore to be endured.

Falls prevention programs are available to all older people and are usually run over a three month period in groups. Find out about their local programs via your loved one's GP or if they have been in hospital, as part of their discharge package.

Medication review

Visit your loved one's health practitioner for a medication review – see if they need a change in dosage or a change to a new medication with increased benefits and fewer negative side effects.

Fall risk assessment

Visit health practitioner for a falls risk assessment. They can conduct a variety of balance, co-ordination and strength tests, to assess vulnerability to falling.

One of the tests they may include is the timed up & go test – where your loved one will be asked to stand up out of their chair without using the chair arms for support, walk three metres, turn around and then sit back down again.

Or they may do a turn 180 test – where they are asked to stand up out of their chair without using the chair arms for support, step forward and turn around and sit back down again. This should usually take four steps or less to complete.

I KNOW THEY'RE YOUR FAVOURITES, DEAR, BUT IT'S FOR THE BEST, HONEST!

Eyesight assessment

Visit an optician for an eye test – see if glasses are required (or a change in prescription if they already have them). Just because a person thinks they can see clearly, doesn't mean that is necessarily the case.

Time management – avoid rushing

Encourage sensible time management. If your loved one allows for plenty of time, and avoids placing huge demands and expectations on themselves with a crowded appointment and engagements book, then they can help reduce the risk of falling over in their rush.

Incontinence management

Try to encourage that any incontinence issues are recognised and dealt with by your loved one as soon as possible. This is because a frequent cause of falls in the home of older people is them trying to rush to the toilet or being distracted by dealing with a toileting-related accident that has already occurred.

Improve nutrition

Encourage your loved ones to eat healthy and nutritious meals that will help strengthen their bones, give them more muscle and keep them at a good, solid weight.

You need to focus on nutrition not only for the normal benefits, but when it comes to falls, an older person who is skinny and falls over is more likely to hurt themselves with a fracture or broken bones than a person with a bit of cushioning on them.

If your loved one eats nutritious meals, they are also helping to keep all their faculties in sharper order, their organs functioning well, with clearer eyesight and sharper hearing.

And a healthy person is a stronger person, who will be better placed to catch themselves to prevent a fall happening in the first place and if they do fall over and end up with an injury, a healthy and strong person will be more likely to make a better, fuller recovery.

External prevention

Given that 65% of falls occur in the home, and that is where you have most control over the environment, our advice is focused on issues in and around your loved one's home.

Again, you aren't expected to do all or most of the following preventative actions, but if you do at least two or three, you will have greatly improved your loved one's safety and everybody's lives.

And if you can action all of the advice, that's fantastic!!

Home risk assessment

The first thing you might organise for your ageing loved one is a home risk assessment by a healthcare professional.

They will observe your loved one in their home performing regular living tasks – using the stairs, transferring on and off their bed, chairs and toilet, getting in and out of their bath – and provide recommendations on improvements to help your loved one and categorically reduce the likelihood of them experiencing a fall in their home. That's categorically reduce the risk.

You have the choice of organising and paying for one yourself, referring them or suggesting they refer themselves to their local healthcare provider, or they may receive an assessment of their needs following a hospital admission as a result of them falling. Yes, that is only after they have had a fall…

Carer Min

An extremely active 91 year old lady, who reared seven children, incurred an unfortunate accident resulting in a broken pelvis. At the time, she was sitting on the edge of her bed, getting dressed, when she slid off the shiny duvet onto the floor. Fortunately, there was a telephone on the bedside table so she rang emergency services. After being inconsistent about wearing her medic alarm before her accident, nowadays she wears it 24/7. In some local authorities your loved one maybe referred to a falls project provided they meet the criteria. Due to limited funding, not everyone will meet the criteria. However, if they have a series of falls, live alone (maybe) and want to remain independent, they may be successful. If accepted for the program and referred to a community team, they will then be allocated a case worker. The case worker will assist them to build up their confidence following an assessment of their needs by a healthcare professional. The case worker will work with them to reach their target goals set at assessment, including for example, walking a specific distance each day and by the end of the program being able to manage public transport etc. This type of project is not available everywhere so it is best to ask your loved one's healthcare practitioner for more information. But as said, it will only be available to those who have a history of falls and are likely to have been admitted to hospital, as the hospital admission will be the trigger for referral. Yes, it's only after they have had a fall...

After the fall is when a free assessment is organised. Excellent. Except, when you consider the physical, emotional and financial impact of a fall on the loved one, their family, the hospital and health services. It's anything but free.

So the question you might consider, is why wait for a fall to happen?

Why wait until yours and your loved one's life may be changed for the worse, in every sense, forever?

So please consider having a risk assessment done and most importantly, if you do receive advice, please then consider what has been recommended.

VERY IMPORTANT ACTION STEPS

Additional actions for around the home are
(in no particular order):

1. Make sure that all stairs have rails on both sides and additional hand rails at top and bottom of stairs if necessary. Also ensure that rails are fitted along landing areas. ☐

2. Make sure that the rails are sturdy enough to take your loved one's body weight. Not the lovely ornamental ones that will peel away from the wall when a butterfly lands on them. ☐

3. Consider installing a stairlift if climbing the stairs is becoming increasingly difficult (e.g. where your loved one gets very out of breath). Obviously an assessment of need by a qualified occupational therapist will be necessary to advise on the best option. Assistance with funding the lift may be possible through your loved one's healthcare provider or through a charity. Their OT will be able to advise. ☐

4. Put down non-slip bath mats in the bathroom – both inside and outside of the bathtub. ☐

5. Consider having a shower chair or bath chair or stool installed. ☐

6. Consider having grab rails put up next to the toilet, the bath tub and in the shower. ☐

7. If your loved one has reduced vision, ensure rails are fitted of a contrasting colour to the tiles. For example, blue or yellow against white tiles are best. ☐

8. If possible, remove talcum powder from the bathroom altogether. ☐

9. Have your loved one carry a mobile phone with them at all times. ☐

10. Make sure there are bright lights throughout the house and soft/non-glare bulbs used in the bathroom (to reduce the glare from the wet surfaces that can affect eyesight). ☐

11. Plug in night lights in the bedroom, hallway and bathroom. ☐

12. Remove loose electrical cords from across the floor. ☐

13. Remove rugs and floor coverings that can be tripped on. Especially the old, frayed variety with curled up edges. ☐

14. Suggest changing all footwear that doesn't provide full, surround foot support. Old slippers are very frequently the cause of falls and should be the first item in the bin. ☐

15. Keep decks and outside areas free of moss and oil or anything else that builds up slowly over time and creates a slippery surface. ☐

16. Keep clutter around the house to a minimum as it is just something else to fall over. ☐

17. Try to avoid having polished or waxed floors. They might look nice and sparkly, but so does a wet ice rink. And neither is any good for older people. ☐

18. Consider getting a seat raiser for the toilet seat for ease in sitting down and getting up and a commode if incontinence is becoming an issue. ☐

19. Look into having beds raised with rails fitted for extra support if appropriate. Seek advice from a healthcare professional. ☐

20. Ensure chairs have sturdy back support and raised or if balance is becoming a particular issue then a riser/recliner chair either powered or manual may be a good option to ensure safe transfers. ☐

21. Check that frequently used goods are in an easily accessible cupboard or wardrobe. ☐

22. Check that a stepladder is available. ☐

23. If mobility has started to become an issue, then it might help to find out about products that help with stability. Walking sticks and walkers come in a huge variety of styles and perform a wide range of functions. And having a simple walking stick to balance might be all that's required to prevent a loved one's fall and potentially save their life. ☐

24. If your loved one is experiencing considerable mobility issues, perhaps a powered vehicle for outdoor use rather than risking life and limb when walking is a good option. ☐

25. And last but not least, you might consider buying or renting a wrist or necklace pendant alarm. The community alert wrist and pendant alarms come into their own when a fall occurs within a loved one's home. We would urge you to remind your loved one that these alarms are to be worn at all times and not left on the table beside the television! ☐

What reason do you have for not actioning at least one of the above suggestions?

Carer Min

As you no doubt have realised, many people are just downright obstinate when it comes to accepting suggestions.

It isn't a surprise though, at how conscientious people become at wearing their medic alarm after they have had a fall and maybe spent a few days in hospital.

This is probably a timely place to mention that people can save themselves quite a bit of stress and potentially critical time, if there is always a hospital bag packed and at the ready, especially if the carer does not live in. Don't overlook having all clothing items and toiletries marked with your loved one's name.

It's not nice making such preparations, but if people are of an age where falls and accidents may occur more frequently the better prepared you and they are, the better off you all will be.

And, let's not forget, falls occur without any warning. It's important to always remain alert and keep reminding your loved one to "watch your step", "hold onto the rail" and most importantly, "take your time stepping in to the shower".

If you would like some more statistics to remind just what an impact a fall can have on the over 65s:

- Approximately 25% of hip fracture patients will make a full recovery
- 40% will require nursing home admission
- 50% will be dependent upon a cane or a walker
- 20% will die in one year

At the risk of being repetitive.

This is why prevention is better than cure.

Fall prevention is absolutely the single most critical topic in this book.

And the most critical tip for you to take action on.

A comprehensive list of resources for Falls Awareness and Falls Prevention-related information as well as safety product and service providers can be found on the Resources page on our website: **www.ActionForAgeing.com/Resources**

We recommend you visit the website of Age UK for advice and resources as well as quality products and services: **www.ageuk.org.uk**

REQUEST

1. Please re-read this whole section.

2. Select at least three tips to action this week!!

3. Select three tips to action next week.

4. Please ask your loved one to consider having a Personal Fall Assessment from their GP.

5. Please ask your loved one to consider having a Home Fall Risk Assessment from an occupational therapist. Now, not after they have had a fall.

6. Suggest some basic and cheap fall prevention products for your ageing loved one's home, such as a non-slip bath mat, a night light for the hallway and non-glare lights for the bathroom. Also, upon the advice and help of professionals, perhaps fit rails inside and outside your loved one's home to help reduce the risk of a fall (and all of the associated hospitalisation and care package bills thereafter).

Remember:

Many of the topics we discuss may seem extreme and irrelevant now, but it's good to read about them anyway because they may well be part of your reality tomorrow.

ACTION STEPS for fall prevention this week

1.

2.

3.

4.

ACTION STEPS for fall prevention next week

1.

2.

3.

4.

ACTION STEPS – falls assessments

1. Medication review. ☐

2. Functional falls risk assessment. ☐

3. Eyesight assessment. ☐

4. Home risk assessment. ☐

Financial planning

> **Fact:** Discussing personal finance, tax, pensions and health care options is all rather boring.

Very important, yet not done

Whilst it is normal for the mention of financial planning, tax advice and retirement and health care planning to make your eyes glaze over as you slowly drift off to sleep, the basic fact is that most people don't bother getting a financial plan in place and therefore most people do not have as financially secure or enjoyable retirement as they might have expected.

The fundamental points here are:

- at some stage we will all need to have services provided to us in our own home or in a care home, funded either by private or public means
- someone will need to pay the health and care bills for your loved ones
- who actually pays the bills will depend on your loved one's financial position
- their financial position will depend on what sort of financial planning has, or has not, taken place
- few people ever think about the care needs of older people until the need for providing or receiving care is upon them
- even fewer people think about it and take action to prepare

The purpose of talking to a financial planner is to:

- discuss with your ageing loved ones what their financial goals are and what their income source is likely to be (private pension or state benefits)

- assist with preparing a budget to manage their income and expenses so that their financial goals can be realised

- review what options are available with respect to health care and what their preference is, given various health and well being scenarios

- make provision for dealing with long term care or death with specifically structured insurance products

- establish what their wishes are with respect to their estate and its distribution, so that the right financial decisions are made to achieve them

- help ensure they (and you) understand what Power of Attorney means whilst they are fully cognisant, and make the necessary preparations now so that in the event that they are deemed incapable of making their own decisions, their true, personal wishes will be reflected and represented

WAKE UP!!

Just in case all that talk of tax, insurance and planning got the better of you, please re-read the above bullet points – just once more.

It is important to think about:

- what financial planning is

- why it is really beneficial for your ageing loved ones to:
    - receive information about planning
    - consider seeking financial planning advice

The reason it's good to take action now on financial planning is because the earlier people get advice, the better prepared their financial affairs will be.

Most people wait until something catastrophic happens, like an accident, before they investigate what their care financing options are.

Why wait until then?

- it's easier to do it when all concerned are not in a state of panic and stress
- gather the necessary information now and make an informed decision

Whilst the alternatives of available products and tools for financial planning are numerous and forever changing, the need for all of us to prepare as best we can is the one constant.

The sooner we do it, the better of we and all our loved ones will be.

If you wish to find out more information about financial planning and professional service providers, please refer to the Resources page on our website: **www.ActionForAgeing.com/Resources**

ACTION STEPS – Financial & care planning

1. Gather information about financial and care planning. ☐

2. Inform your ageing loved ones about the benefits of planning. ☐

3. Identify a professional, trustworthy financial planner. ☐

4. Where possible, meet with the planner and receive information and advice. ☐

5. Discuss the options available. ☐

6. Where appropriate, take action and prepare for the future. ☐

TOPIC 19

Fire prevention

Fact: In the UK, there are 65,000 house fires per year (one every eight minutes).

Fact: 26% of fires in the home occur whilst cooking, which = 13,000 fires per year.

Fact: Fires in the home account for 75% of all fire-related deaths.

Fact: Over 50% of those killed in house fires are over 65.

Old dog, safer tricks

We all get into bad habits over our lifetime and by the time we get to our later years we may well have a few entrenched habits that increase the chances of creating a house fire.

When we are young we might be able to get away with bad fire safety habits because we are more alert, have quicker reflexes, better balance and co-ordination and have sharper senses of smell, sight and hearing.

As we get older however, whether we like it or not, these senses often become impaired. And your loved one is no different. (Nor, by the way, are we.)

Carer Min

My aunt, who was in her 70's and lived by herself in the family home, had forgotten to pay the power bill, resulting in the power being cut off.

She enjoyed reading in bed at night and her solution to having no power was to have a large candle set into a candle holder sitting on the mattress near her head.

On this particular night she fell asleep, the candle fell over and she awoke to find her mattress on fire. Luck was truly on her side because she was able to put the fire out with the assistance of a couple of blankets.

Her daughter was horrified when she learnt of this event and she promptly arranged a work transfer from another city, which enabled her to move back home to care for her mother, for the next twenty years.

Another family story. A squatter in his 60's had taken up residence in a totally dilapidated, unlived in house that belonged to a family member. The family member knew that he was living there but decided to let him stay there undisturbed.

One night the squatter was walking down the hallway using a candle to light his way. Suddenly the floorboards gave way and he went sliding through.

> *The candle set fire to his beard and, after much bellowing on his part, assistance arrived. The following day he contacted a solicitor and asked him to assist him to sue the owner (my relative) because the house he was squatting in had proved to be unsafe and he wanted some sort of reimbursement for his burnt beard.*
>
> *Fortunately, he was sent on his way empty handed. Unfortunately, the fire damage to the house and its dilapidated state meant that it was bulldozed a short time later.*

What is very helpful is if we take an honest and frank look at our daily habits and identify where we are taking unnecessary risks regarding fire danger.

You may not be able to teach an old dog new tricks, but we can still be reminded that our old tricks could end up getting us fried!!

Carer Min

Many years ago whilst working in community care, I regularly visited a delightful couple, Mary and Joe, who both had dementia.

Mary still prepared their evening meal which often comprised lamb chops, fried in an open pan.

Every visit I patiently removed the tea towel which hung over the oven door, the oven being placed directly above the hotplates.

I would remove the tea towel and place it on a hook beside the kitchen sink, meanwhile explaining to Mary that it could catch fire if it remained hanging above the hotplates.

Mary would readily agree. Each time I returned to visit, the tea towel was back hanging above the hotplates.

One day I arrived and they weren't at home. Upon enquiring, I discovered the tea towel had caught fire and the kitchen had been gutted.

Fortunately, Mary and Joe had alerted the neighbours whose prompt action led to the rest of the house being saved.

I had advised my superiors months before of this potential hazard and as this was many years ago, at that time there was legally nothing else that anyone could do.

Nowadays, actions such as a risk assessment may take place, with the cooker being turned off and replaced by a microwave. Unfortunately, Carer Min's tale is far from unique.

Don't forget:

- 26% of fires in the home occur whilst cooking, which translates to 13,000 fires per year.
- In the UK there are 65,000 house fires per year (one every eight minutes), with fires in the home accounting for 75% of all fire-related deaths (600 per year).

And sadly, over half of those 600 who die in accidental house fires are over sixty-five years old.

Here are a few tips to remember for your loved one's home.

- Take note of how the door is locked and also how to unlock it. The reason for this is that, generally speaking, people tend to keep all of their doors securely locked. If, by chance, a fire did occur, you need to know how to get out of there as fast as possible.
- When a fire gains hold there is roughly forty seconds to exit the property. Not because of the fire itself, but because of the effect of the fumes.
- Check to see if your loved one has a combination smoke and carbon monoxide alarm installed. They cost £20 and take five minutes to screw in. It's the smoke rather than the fire itself that usually causes injury/death. It's recommended to test the alarm regularly to ensure it's still working. The battery life depends on the model, and it's best to be vigilant.
- If your loved ones have lived in their house for many years, ask an electrician check the wiring, plugs, sockets and the like, because if any are frayed, overloaded or in a state of near disrepair, it is better to get them repaired before an accident occurs.
- Check they have a readily available fire blanket and extinguisher, in a very central location. This is critical.

- Suggest your loved one removes old newspapers and old magazines that are no longer needed, rather than allowing them to pile up and become fuel if a fire occurs.

- Some ageing loved ones have a tendency to hoard old shoes, clothing, empty boxes saved from purchases made many years ago, plastic takeaway containers and anything else they consider that is "too good to throw out" or "might come in handy one day". If your loved one is a bit of a hoarder (or a lot of a hoarder) maybe suggest they donate what is not being used to a local charity. If all of the items must be kept, try and ensure they are being stored in a safe way. All of that can represent a fire hazard as fuel for fire and smoke or by blocking a swift exit.

Carer Min

I have encountered a variety of storage systems in my community work, some of which almost defied imagination when considered in the light of presenting possible fire hazards.

One client's bedroom, in my mind, could only be considered as a possible death trap. I stood in the doorway and my eyes swept around the room.

I had no idea what colour the walls were because I could not see them. Floor to ceiling, against all the walls, were plastic shopping bags loaded with goodness knows what.

Before I could make the bed buried in the middle of the room, I had to remove more bags, books, magazines, sweet wrappers, clothing and the dog!

The client kept telling me to make sure I put everything back in the right place. The contents of the bedroom represented a huge fire hazard, but of course people have the right to organise their home as they wish.

As the spouse, child or friend of your loved one, you might be in a slightly better bargaining position!

Another older gentleman I used to visit was a WW2 veteran who had spent three years as a prisoner of war (POW) in Changi prison camp. Whilst in the camp he was in charge of supplies.

The first time I visited him he was very wary of inviting me in, however his daughter had been keen for him to receive regular visits, so I stood my ground. When I finally stepped through the door I was met with an absolutely amazing sight.

As he led me through the house I was surrounded by an eerie light, coming from hundreds of smouldering mosquito coils. The house lay in darkness apart from the light emanating from the coils.

The gentleman guided me to what he referred to as his "supply depot". After opening the door the gentleman stood back to allow me to enter. He turned on the light and I was looking at a mini supermarket, complete with shelves to the ceiling.

His daughter later explained to me that her father and his fellow prisoners, had been severely affected by mosquitoes in the POW camp and he had formed a lifelong obsession with avoiding being bitten by them.

She also told me that her father had been the officer in charge of the supply depot in Changi and had never really forgiven himself for not having sufficient food for his fellow prisoners. Therefore, he had resolved to always have plenty of supplies on hand if they were needed.

As I grew to know this lovely man I felt honoured to be one of his carers. He had spent his life caring for his fellow prisoners, long after they had returned home.

A critical part of safety in the home is fire prevention. and at the risk of sounding like a broken record...

Prevention is better than cure

The list of ways in which fires can start is limited only by the imagination.

But the list of key fire prevention steps is relatively short and relatively inexpensive (and listed below!)

These are all things that you will already know, but many, many people fail to act on the information. That is the crazy thing about us. We all know what should be done and we know how to do it, with all sorts of life options and decisions. Yet we frequently don't follow that up with the action. Hopefully this is a mindset and behavior that we can all improve on or change over time.

If you would like to find out more about fire safety products, please refer to our Resources page for specialist suppliers. **www.ActionForAgeing.com/Resources**

ACTION STEPS – Fire Prevention

1. Review home habits and try to curb the bad fire hazards. ☐

2. Raise awareness and remind about fire dangers. ☐

3. Check exit paths and door locks for easy, speedy exit. ☐

4. Purchase and install a smoke and carbon monoxide detector as a gift. They cost £20 and take 5 minutes to screw in. Better than a bunch of flowers! ☐

5. Once the detector is installed, it's good to remind your loved one to check the battery every three months. ☐

6. Check that a fire extinguisher and fire blanket are stored in a central location. ☐

7. Suggest your loved one donate or store safely any unused/hoarded goods that can add fuel to a fire or block a safe exit. ☐

8. Check if it worth having the electrical wiring inspected by an electrician. Faulty wiring, sockets and plugs are not uncommon in older people's houses, especially as they may have gone decades with little or no maintenance. ☐

9. It is good to review the simple fire safety steps with your loved ones and to take action where needed or as a precaution (that is the important bit!). ☐

Footwear

> **Fact:** Slippers, especially once old and worn, can be lethal.

It's all in the name – slippers

Your ageing loved one has probably walked a lot of miles over the years so it is only right that they wear comfortable footwear.

Remember that as we age and our bodies change, we need to adjust our buying habits. With shoes, ensuring that your loved ones have pairs that are comfortable and suitable is a priority. For example, shoe laces can be more of a challenge to older people because their fingers aren't as nimble as they used to be, or they get dizzy bending over to do up the laces.

Carer Min

As you may well have discovered, older people are often loathe to spend money on themselves.

I've so often heard the comment, "These shoes, or slippers, will see me out".

They may well hasten their departure if their footwear doesn't fit them properly and they over balance and fall.

Shoes with laces are to be avoided where possible. Velcro is a wonderful invention because of its ability to provide a secure fit to both shoes and slippers.

YES, MAVIS, THE SIXTIES WERE A LOT OF FUN... BUT PERHAPS IT'S TIME TO PUT THE BOOTS AWAY.

Loose fitting, sloppy footwear, like an old pair of slippers, provides older people with an invitation to trip over mats and rugs around their home.

Slippers are called slippers not just because they are easy to slip into, but if old and worn and have no back on them, they are easy to slip out of too. Great if someone is getting into bed. Not so great if someone is going down the stairs.

Steps and stairs themselves also present a challenge if incorrect footwear is being worn. Where carpets become frayed, they can catch shoe soles and cause a fall. Or polished floor boards can act as an ice skating rink for a smooth-bottomed pair of slippers.

Overly-grippy rubber soles are also to be avoided, because older people have a tendency to shuffle and the rubber soles grip the ground and trip the wearer over.

It might be worth suggesting your loved one has a rummage through their footwear collection and remove the shoes that may cause them to trip or slip.

A new pair of good quality slippers makes for a great Christmas, birthday or 'Thinking of You' present.

The price it will cost to replace a dangerous pair of shoes is far less than the cost of one night in hospital, let alone weeks of care and rehabilitation.

It seems obvious and yet people don't do it.

To involve your loved one in the shoe review, perhaps try throwing it into the conversation the next time you are speaking on the phone and see where it leads?

There are all sorts of specialised shoes, sandals and boots available from chemist shops and department stores that are very comfortable to wear around the home and outside and especially designed with the requirements of older people (and they aren't all dull, clunky, beige things – although they are probably available if that look appeals!).

There are also items such as long-handled shoe horns that make putting shoes on much easier.

If you would like to find out more about footwear products please visit our Resources page at: **www.ActionForAgeing.com/ Resources**

ACTION STEPS – Footwear

1. Suggest your loved one review their footwear. Throw out whatever is loose or worn, has overly-grippy rubber soles or is a potential source of a slip. ☐

2. Check your loved one's house to see if any of the home features represent a risk, given the footwear worn in the house. ☐

3. Where possible, introduce velcro secured footwear. ☐

4. For lace-up shoes, introduce elasticised laces and use a long-handled show horn so that the shoes effectively become slip-ons! ☐

5. Switch the old house slippers for a comfy, full-heeled non-slip variety. ☐

The fridge

> **Fact:** No one thinks cleaning the fridge is fun.

Check the date on everything

This is not necessarily unique to ageing loved ones, as we all have things that were once food crawling about on the back shelf or shivering in the deepest corner of the vegetable drawer.

However, as we age, our eyesight or other senses can gradually become dulled and therefore we are more at risk of eating something that is long past its expiry date that might make us ill.

As a current or future carer (in whatever capacity), one of the regular actions that is needs to be performed is:

• Check the fridge and remove any food past its use-by date.

And when we say regularly, we mean regularly, because it is often the case that older people can have products stored in their fridge that are months and sometimes even years, out of date (as can we all).

Of course, most people are perfectly capable of organising their fridge. We simply mention the subject for the special loved ones, like those who have been diagnosed with dementia or are in its early stages, who are at the more vulnerable end of the ageing spectrum.

Carer Min

When doing a fridge contents review, some people will stay right beside me, carefully checking what I am up to. I include them in the decision making.

"Vera. This bread has mould on it. Is it all right for me to let it go?" By including the people in the decision making, I have found that one accomplishes far more than simply bulldozing your way in.

I have witnessed some relatives who try the bulldozing approach, with the result that their loved one feels intimidated and resentful. Not the win-win scenario that we should always be aiming for.

The biggest trap I have found as a carer is when the older person says to me, "Don't worry, I'll do it after you've gone. It'll give me something to do". Next time I visit? The fridge contents are exactly as I last saw them.

If your loved one wants to run their fridge at peak efficiency (i.e. at lowest cost), then keeping the fridge three-quarters full is better than it being empty. At three-quarters full, the fridge more easily maintains its cool temperature as food and drinks on the shelves block warm air that rushes in each time the door is opened.

Cool fridge tips

If the refrigerator stinks:

- Locate the offending items and give the inside a good wipe with a soft cloth that has been soaked in a mixture of vanilla essence and cold water.

- Food in the fridge will keep for longer if it is stored in airtight plastic boxes like Tupperware.
- It's better to wash fresh fruit and vegetables just before use rather than after buying them and putting them in the refrigerator. Moisture from washing can accelerate the ageing and moulding process, causing food to go off sooner.

Carer Min

As a carer I have found that when relatives/friends arrive with a simple supply of milk, cheese, bread and butter it is often greatly appreciated by their loved one.

Many older people survive on very meagre rations and often nutrition is seriously neglected and not realised by family members who do not live nearby or visit frequently.

In my experience, most clients who rely on government sponsored support have very little money, even for essentials.

As many older people are on a tight budget, if you bring lunch or dinner with you, they are usually very appreciative!

They enjoy a fresh, hearty, free meal with no hassle of preparation or cleaning up and you can enjoy their company.

If you would like more information about refrigerator management, or the suppliers of food preservation products like Tupperware, please visit the resources page on our website: **www.ActionForAgeing.com/Resources**

ACTION STEPS – Refrigerator management

1. Check the fridge and remove any food past its use-by date. ☐

2. Keeping the fridge three-quarters full is a more economical way to run it, than it being empty. ☐

3. Check if your loved one has good quality food preservation containers. ☐

4. Wash fresh fruit and veggies only when about to eat them. ☐

5. Try to take a supply of staple foods with you when visiting. ☐

6. You'll be very popular if you offer to bring a meal with you!! ☐

TOPIC 22

Gadgets and aid items

The list below contains a small selection of the many products that are available to help improve the safety and wellbeing of our ageing loved ones.

Most don't cost very much and although they might not seem relevant now, it's worth having a look anyway. Who who knows what gadget or product might be very handy in the future?

House

Key turner – Connects to the end of most keys and provides a larger grip with which to turn the key. Looks a bit like a boomerang, but if you throw the keys, they won't do a loop and come flying back.

Letterbox basket – Is fitted inside your front door and catches mail, so there is no need to bend over picking mail up from the floor. The basket also helps prevent intruders using the letter box to unlock the door. They will however, be able to leave you a note commending you on your security.

Extended reacher – A long stick with claw on the end that enables people to pick up small objects that are out of easy reach. Also useful for placing clothes on the top shelf of wardrobes and performing key-hole heart surgery. Okay, one of the last two uses was not true. But the extendable reacher is quite handy for lots of other things!

Handle/knob-turner – Fits over a door handle or door knob, providing a larger handle to grip and turn. If the door is locked, the handle-turner doesn't really help. Unless you use it to break a window.

Household trolley – Small trolley with trays on it that can be used to help people carry items around the house. Please note: They are not designed for use as a mobility aid so should never be used to perform that function. They shouldn't be raced down hallways either.

Flashing-vibrating door-bell – Helps to know when visitors arrive. Many come with a small belt attachment, so can be worn. Whether a variety of colours is available to match people's attire of the day will depend on the brand.

Milk bottle holder – Long handled variety saves bending down to pick up the milk bottles. Can also be used as a putter for indoor golf with a piece of rolled up newspaper in the living room.

Carton-holder – A holder that fits around a juice or milk carton that has a large handle to make gripping and pouring easier. It won't however, make grapefruit juice taste any less tart.

Cream/white lamp shades – Keeping lighting bright around the home is one of the best ways to help prevent falls. It helps keep stairs and items that can be tripped over, visible. Nightlights along the hallway and in the bathroom help with safe movement at night time. A blind fold, ear plugs and hands cuffed behind the back do not.

Telephones – With extra large buttons or cordless phones that can be carried. Also BT have a variety of phones with features such as extra loud rings, inbound and outbound amplifiers, phones with flashing lamps and more. Further, a text-telephone service is available from national charity groups. Cordless headsets are also available so that people can walk around the house with their hands free and prepare dinner whilst chatting. Not to be used in the shower (or whilst on the toilet, thanks very much). Please refer to 'Telephones' on the Resources page of our website **www.ActionForAgeing.com**

Hand-held cordless vacuum cleaner – To help make cleaning stairs and other cleaning jobs quicker and easier than using a dustpan and brush. Some models have attachments to make them longer, to reduce the need for bending over when in use. No models come with a fold-out hot drinks holder.

Anti-slip matting – To help keep mats in place so they don't move and become items that can be tripped over or slipped on. Where they got the name for this product is anyone's guess.

Message in a bottle – Scheme supported by Lions Club International whereby people keep their personal medical details written on a short form and kept in a small plastic bottle in their refrigerator. In the case of an emergency at home where a person is unconscious or unable to effectively communicate, the emergency services are able to immediately retrieve that person's details from the bottle. Please refer to our topic 'Message in a Bottle' on page 253.

Smoke and Carbon Monoxide Alarms – Smoke and carbon monoxide alarms – Potentially life-saving, take five minutes to install and a good quality dual alarm costs under £20! When putting a new battery in or testing the alarm, be sure to be ready for the siren, because they are LOUD and even when you know it is coming, it still scares people.

Electric plugs – If gripping plugs becomes a problem, plugs used regularly (e.g. on kettle) can be replaced with a loop-handled plug, a plastic T-piece plug or have a plastic strip attached to the original plug, that makes it easier to pull. If someone wants to change the plug themselves, they need to remember that the green wire means... or was it that the red wire means... they should always seek the services of a professional tradesperson.

High voltage, long life light bulbs – Using bright light bulbs in the centre of the room will help with visibility and using the long life variety will be cheaper in the long run. And they need to be changed less often, reducing risks associated with climbing about on dining chairs trying to change a bulb.

Pendant/wrist alarms – Most widely known of the assistive technology products. The jam sandwich of the Telecare world. Please refer to the topic 'Pendant & wrist alarms' on page 275 and also the topic 'Technology/Telecare' on page 309.

TV and video/DVD Remote Control – Versions with extra large buttons, a reduced number of buttons to help avoid confusion or where a single remote can operate the TV and video/DVD player are available. If the inventors can find a way to stop a remote control from sliding down the back of the sofa, that would be very handy too!

Chair raiser – If a frequently used, favourite lounge chair is too low, they can become very difficult for older bodies to get up from. Proper chair raisers, rather than a pile of bricks, is the safest solution.

Standing frames – A frame that can be positioned next to a chair to help create leverage for rising out of the seat with. Most frames are adjustable. None are made from bananas.

Magnifying glass – To help with reading books, newspaper and instructions (and use-by dates!) where the font is particularly small. People can also raise the magnifying glass to their eye to make their eye look enormous and scare small children.

Kitchen

Long-handled dustpan and brush – Will help prevent risks associated with bending over. Won't cure baldness.

Fire blanket – Kept in the kitchen. To be used to throw over an accidental fire. Not something you lay on whilst roasting marshmellows.

Talking microwave oven – These microwaves have speaking controls and reminders and come with instructions that are available in large print or an audio product. A special audio book of recipes for the audio microwave also comes with some models. Maybe if you select 'TV Celebrity Head Chef' mode, the microwave will scream the recipe at you and use all sorts of swear words.

Slip-resistant mat – A large or small square of non-slip mat that sits on the kitchen workbench that can be used to work on. The mat stops mixing bowls from slipping off the smooth bench surface and helps stop ingredients such as eggs from rolling off onto the floor. So it acts as a Falls Prevention tool as well. Bonus!

Perching stool – Some have back rests and arm rests too. Look for a model that has non-slip feet. When sitting in one, you will feel like a tennis umpire.

Step-stool – Helps in reaching the high shelf and can add a long handle for improved safety. Not to be used as a piece of gym equipment.

Saucepans with easy grip – A large variety of saucepans are available that have different shaped handles and grips for easier use. This makes them easier to use for cooking and beating intruders over the head.

Kettle-tipper – Product that a kettle can be strapped into, to assist in pouring. Especially useful when a wrist has become weakened by an injury or arthritis. Not to be confused with cow tipping. Which is purportedly when drunk, rural teenagers run around paddocks in the dark pushing over sleeping cows.

Kitchen utensils with easy grip – A range of kitchen utensils are available that have handles that are easier to grip. These can be spatulas, carving knives and forks, cheese cutters, scissors and bread knives to name but a few.

Electric can opener – Makes life easier. Simple as that really.

Jar gripper – Rubber pad to help grip and open jars. If sleight of hand is used, people can still pretend they are using raw power to open the jar with their bare hands.

Tap-turners – Plastic handle that fits over the water tap to make it easier to grip and turn. Very 'handy', so to speak.

Water taps with long handles – If new taps are being installed, consider getting a model that has a long handle. Or those hand-sensor fittings with no taps – just a ray of light – if there are huge bags of cash sitting around the house.

Free-hand tray – A tray with a handle looped over the top, so that food or drinks can be carried more easily, leaving a free hand for using stair hand rails, etc. Models with a fold-down handle make for easy storage. Okay for transporting a cup of coffee. Not so good for 12 champagne glasses.

Lap tray – These provide a level surface and some models come with a small bean bag attached underneath for improved stability. Handy for small jigsaws too.

Dinner plates – Special dinner plates are available with a high, curled lip that helps prevent spillage and makes eating with one hand easier. A plate surround is also available, which clips on to the edge of a regular dinner plate. The high, curled lip of the surround also makes eating with one hand easier and scooping up the last of the peas a quicker job.

Bedroom

Back-rests – To help make sitting up in bed more comfortable, different models of back rests are available. Rigid backrests with adjustable frames or V-shaped cushion back rests.

Neck pillows – Inflatable or filled already with beads, gel or some other product, neck pillows can help provide support, especially when sitting up in bed. They look like a big, inflated horseshoe and are actually more comfortable than they might appear!

Bed Elevators – To raise the head or foot of the bed to provide pain relief from swollen ankles... or heads. If they are placed in the middle of the bed, well... that will be very uncomfortable.

Bed trays – To provide a flat work surface or a tray table to eat from. Not advisable for building a house of cards on or to be ridden on through the snow.

Over-bed tables – These are a large tray attached to a frame with free-standing legs that go from under the bed on the floor and wrap around up the side and over the top of the bed. The tray provides a flat and stable surface to eat or work from, whilst sitting up in bed. Very helpful!

Hot water/warmer bottles – Instead of traditional hot water bottles that present a risk of hot water burns, there are many new types of warmers that can be heated up in a microwave in a few seconds and stay warm for hours. Some models can also be put in the freezer and can act as a cold pack for an injury or swelling. The warmers use gel or some other high-tech material that is securely contained within the warmer cover. There are even mini versions that can be put in a coat pocket on a cold winter day. Whoever comes up with such products are very clever people.

Dressing-stick – Where dressing has become increasingly difficult, a dressing stick may be of help. They are a thin, two foot long pole with a hook at the end that can be used to guide clothing on. If the household has two dressing-sticks, the can also be used as novelty salad servers (for a very big salad).

Long-handled shoe horn – Just like a short one in the shoe shop, but two feet longer!

Elastic shoe laces – Turns lace-up shoes into slip-ons and when used with a long-handled shoe horn, helps avoid the bending over and potential dizziness of tying standard shoe laces. Would be helpful for school kids too.

Bathroom

Hot water detectors – To help avoid burns because of hot water in the bath tub, a Hotspot Detector can be hung along the inside of the bath. The detector will change colour with the water temperature so as to indicate if the bath water is too hot. If the detector melts and shrivels up, then probably best to let the water cool for a bit.

Digital thermometer – These can be attached to the side of the bath to give a more precise reading of the water temperature. Some may even sound an alarm or play a tune. None will make a decent coffee.

Long-handled sponges and washers – Large variety of washing items, such as sponges or scrubbing brushes that can help people wash the harder-to-reach places. North and South of the border.

Medication reminders – Alarms that remind people to take medication. Some even have a tray that will automatically release the dosage required for the particular day and also time of day. A person's GP can recommend what medication procedure is most suitable.

Bath rails – Can be fixed to a wall or edge of the bathtub. Help getting into and out of a bathtub and also provide support if someone is to slip. That's physical support. As far as emotional support goes, the bath rail might be a good listener, but not much in the way of discussion. Please refer to the Topic: 'Bathroom safety' on page 45 for more information.

Bath steps – Small box-like step with a non-slip surface that can be placed outside the bathtub, making it easier to enter and exit the bathtub. Much more graceful than clambering over the side of the tub.

Bath boards – These boards sit across the bathtub and can be locked into position, to provide support for people getting into and out of the bathtub, from a seated position. Not to be confused with boogie boards that you use for riding the waves at the beach.

Bath mats – A must-have for EVERY household. Inside the bathtub (and outside too ideally) they can help prevent people from slipping over in the bath. These should be handed out for free to everyone over 60 years old. We will do our best! Please refer to our topic 'Bathroom safety' on page 45.

Bath seats – A small seat for inside the bath. Check that the seat has feet that will grip the surface of the bathtub, as it is vital that the seat remains secured in position. Next on the inventor's list can be a bath coffee table and we can splash around in a cafe.

Bath cushions – These come in a variety of styles, filled with air, foam, gel or some other material. Check that the cushion has grippers or suckers on the back, so that the cushion will remain fixed where you attach it. A cushion that shifts about when you do or goes floating off down the bathtub isn't much help. Whether there are bath cushion covers with pictures of dog's heads on them is yet to be confirmed.

Grab-rail – Having a grab-rail installed in the shower or bath provides a secure fitting to hold on to in case of a slip/fall or to provide leverage when entering or exiting. Between bath times, it's an extra place to hand a towel.

Shower stool – Can be square or a triangle shaped stool that is waterproof and sits in the corner of the shower. Helps if someone feels dizzy from the heat or if they find standing up in the shower is too difficult. They come in all shapes and sizes. Much the same as people's bottoms.

Shower seat – These are seats that flip out from the wall of the shower. When they are not in use they can fold back up against the wall. Mind fingers!

Toilet seat-raiser – If people are finding it difficult lowering onto and rising from a regular height toilet, they might like to use a toilet seat raiser. These are adjustable up to six inches or more and help to raise the toilet seat to the optimum height for the user. Much easier than having the bathroom floor lowered.

Toilet frame – A four-legged frame that fits around the toilet and has handle bars on either side. The handle bars can act as arm rests whilst the person is seated using the toilet and used to provide leverage to get up from the toilet when finished. It may look a little like gym equipment, but the swing and centre dismount might get quite messy.

Bottom wipers – These small devices provide a simple and hygienic way to assist people with bottom wiping. The toilet paper can be easily attached, used and disposed of. Not something people often think about until it's needed, but definitely a helpful one to remember!

Garden

Please refer to our topic 'Gardening' on page 177 for tips on creating an age-friendly and back-friendly garden.

Knee pads – Helps with comfort and keeping clean and dry whilst people are getting down and dirty in the garden.

Kneeler stool – Can be used to sit on whilst gardening or can be used to help people get up or down from their kneeling position. Very handy item for green-fingered older folk!

Gardening tools – There are a wide variety of gardening tools available with a modified grip or handle to make usage easier for older people whose strength or agility may not be quite what it once was. There are also special grips that can be attached to regular tools to make usage easier or long-handled tools to reduce the need to bend over, kneel or stretch.

Support-cuff – Like the arm cuff on a modern crutch, a support cuff can be attached to a long handled tool to provide even greater comfort for the user. Comfort all round!

Long-reach pruning tool – These are regular pruning tools but with a telescopic handle.

Roll-out Trackway – A roll of non-slip outdoor carpet that can be rolled across gravel or lawn to provide a flatter, more secure surface to walk on. It looks like a landing strip, but rather ironically, is invented to prevent people from landing... on their backside whilst out in the garden.

If you would like to find out more information about these products and other gadgets and aids designed to help your ageing loved ones and promote their wellbeing, please visit our website Resources page **www.ActionForAgeing.com**

Gardening

> **Fact:** Ageing can bring reduced strength and flexibility in people's backs and knees.
>
> **Fact:** Your loved one's garden may need to be modified accordingly.

Start modification now

Many people have been prolific gardeners in times past.

However, as aching joints take their toll, they are unable to kneel to tend their gardens and so once bountiful, thriving flower and vegetable plots become somewhat dilapidated.

It therefore makes sense for you to ask your loved one to look at their garden and answer the following question:

"If you couldn't kneel down, how much of your garden could you tend?" 80%? 50%? 10%?

If the garden is their pride and joy, and they want to spend as much of their time in it as possible, it is worth taking action to modify their garden so that in the years to come, as they become less agile, they will still be able to continue enjoying gardening for as long as possible.

ACTION step – START modification of the garden NOW.

It's not a case of removing the whole garden and replacing it with concrete and plastic plants (although that is a very low maintenance option). But it makes sense to start planning for changes now that will ensure the garden remains accessible in the future.

Like much of what we've said elsewhere in this book: preparation is the key. It makes sense to modify the garden now, rather than wait to make it age-friendly when you have to, e.g. due to an injury.

If your loved one is unable to make the modifications themselves, alternatives include:

- paying a professional gardener (potentially expensive!)
- seek the help of a local charity or association
- call in friends and family to help

The second and third options are great activities for people to share together.

Remember, one in three over sixty-fives suffer a reported fall every year. That means that 3.4 million people may lose their ability to tend their garden, because they can't kneel down.

It's best not to wait until such an injury happens. With garden modification, as with all preparations for ageing, the sooner it's done, the better!

Questions to consider:

- what work can be done in the garden from a standing or seated position?
- can ground covering be made more low maintenance, by replacing grass with paving stones or decking?
- can plants that require daily or weekly tending be replaced with hardier, self-sufficient plants?
- are there shrubs and trees that require considerable strength to be able to maintain them that can be replaced with low maintenance alternatives?
- can the level of the garden be raised, so as to minimise or ideally eradicate the need to kneel down or bend over?

- can paths be widened and lowered below the garden level, to provide easier access and help someone tending from a standing or seated position?
- are the paths easy to slip on?
- are there steps that can be taken out and replaced by a gradual slope?
- can steps be made more visible or be lowered if the steps are quite deep?

In short: What can be done to the garden to enable people to continue spending time in it tomorrow, when their body is not as agile as it is today?

The KEY steps are to be CREATIVE and ACT NOW.

If people establish their low maintenance garden over time, in the years ahead they can take pleasure from tending the garden without actually being required to do the

THE DOCTOR SAYS GARDENING IS GOOD FOR HIS BLOOD PRESSURE.

amount of work they do now. An important point, as in future, your loved one won't be as flexible and strong as they are now.

It is also worth considering planting flower/vegetable seedlings in window boxes, which are placed waist high, either on tables, wheelbarrows, or any raised space which is available.

Carer Min

There is something very primal and satisfying about working with someone to set up a small garden, even on a mini window box scale.

And it's certainly true in my experience that herbs that you have grown yourself in your own little flower box taste a lot better than the herbs you might buy in a supermarket.

Window boxes are especially good for people who use walkers or wheelchairs.

Gardening on a budget? No problem. Grow plants in old ice cream containers, or plastic takeaway pots or anything that will hold a plant, instead of actual window boxes. Why not use a small, old cupboard turned on its side, an old bucket or half barrel or wooden chest?

If you take a walk around a second-hand furniture shop and look for old furniture that can be modified into an interesting planter or window box, you might be surprised at what suddenly appears.

Again, it's an opportunity to be creative.

There are also the added benefits of introducing more planters and window boxes into your loved one's home:

- vegetables or herbs grown at home are a lot cheaper than those paid for at the supermarket.
- tending plants in a planter or within a window box arrangement can provide many happy hours of free activity.
- gardening is good exercise.

Gardens provide a sense of having a responsibility and sense of nurturing and it's a good excuse to get outside in the fresh air.

The main point with respect to older people and their garden is to remind them that they will not be as agile in future as they are now. If they start thinking about what modifications they can make and start taking action now, then they can help maximise the time in the future that they will be able to continue enjoying their gardening activity. Don't wait until they are suddenly unable to tend their garden to address this issue.

If you wish to find out more about garden modifications, window box advice or suppliers of garden products, please visit our Resources page on our website: **www.ActionForAgeing.com/ Resources**

Remember:

Although a topic in the book may not seem relevant to you and your loved ones today, it is worth reading because it may be useful in the future.

ACTION STEPS – Gardens

1. Remind your loved one that they will not be agile forever. ☐

2. Assess their garden for high maintenance plants and shrubs. ☐

3. Identify where a low maintenance solution is possible. ☐

4. Replace steps with a gentle slope where possible. ☐

5. Modify deep steps and make them more visible. ☐

6. Raise the garden, where possible, to reduce the need for kneeling. ☐

7. Have paths widened and/or lowered to allow easier access. ☐

8. Make sure ground surfaces are as non-slip as possible. ☐

9. Introduce planters and window boxes that are easy to tend. ☐

10. Start the garden modification now. ☐

Hand rails / grab bars

> **Fact:** There are an estimated 13.4 million falls by over 65s each year = 36,000 falls every day
>
> **Fact:** One in three falls are preventable.

Another simple change – another big impact

Given there are 3.4 million reported falls and a further estimated 10 million unreported falls, it is reasonable to guess that the number of near falls is likely to be numbered in the tens of millions.

With those numbers, it makes sense that you suggest having hand rails installed around your loved one's home: in the bath, the shower, the toilet, the stairway and anywhere else that they are at particular risk of slipping over.

It's best to not wait for your loved one to show obvious signs of being vulnerable to have this discussion. As often as not, the first sign of beingvulnerable is falling over!

Why not be proactive, instead of reactive?

Carer Min

I was once assisting a frail person to have a shower because he'd just come out of hospital and was pretty shaky on his legs. There were no hand rails in the shower recess so he was trying to stay upright by holding onto the shower head.

Holding up his own body weight with the shower head? I think it's a minor miracle that he had survived as long as he had. Goodness knows how many near misses he had had before finally toppling over.

That particular situation was remedied very quickly by organising hand rails and a shower chair to be installed. But what about the people who are at home by themselves, with nobody to help them?

The frustrating thing is that his hand rails and shower chair were only installed AFTER he had already had a fall and been in hospital!?!

We know that right now there are millions of older people in the UK, literally millions, who are also grabbing hold of bathroom or toilet fittings for support to stop them falling over when they should be using a properly secured hand rail.

The rails need to be installed by a person with technical knowledge who is following the advice provided from a healthcare professional on the correct location and positioning of the rails. For example, If they are too high, then it can be difficult to maintain a firm grip and if the rail is too low, it will not provide the leverage required.

We all need to ask ourselves, "Why don't I find out about having handrails installed in my loved one's bathroom?" Next to the toilet, around the bathtub and inside the shower. And if they can have a rubber coating along the rail for improved grip, even better!! If the answer is, "Because of the cost" then we need to think about what the cost of an older person falling over will be to everyone concerned, physically, financially and emotionally.

After these considerations, handrails usually look pretty cheap in comparison. It's so simple, relatively inexpensive and so completely obvious and yet it's not being done until after people have had a fall.

If your loved one is not eligible for items to be provided by the State, there are a number of charities and organisations who might be able to assist with the cost of the purchase and installation of the handrails.

It's also important to note that the installation of handrails should always be performed by a trained professional.

Why wait?

If you want to find out more about handrails, suppliers, installers, charities and associations that can help with funding/installation or contact details for healthcare professionals who can help with your queries, please visit the Resources page on our website **www.ActionForAgeing.com/Resources**

ACTION STEPS – Hand rails / grab bars

1. Don't wait until someone has a fall. Suggest they have handrails installed now. ☐

Health care planning

> **Fact:** Planning for the unexpected (that is actually kind-of expected) is a sensible thing to do.
>
> **Fact:** Health cash plans can be started from as little as £10 per month.

When it comes to health care planning, the options people have available are essentially a variety of insurances. Rather than going along day-to-day and then having to manage the cost of medical or health bills such as the dentist or optometrist as they pop up, people can have a health cash plan to help cover the expense. Or if people have a more serious illness, if they have taken out private medical insurance then that will help avoid potential delays for appointments and treatments and allow them the option of seeking treatment at a private facility.

The cost of private medical insurance depends on a variety of factors based on who is looking to be covered and what they are looking to be covered for. Some policies provide only for the cost of treatment while people are in hospital whilst other policies will also cover outpatient expenses. People pay an insurance premium every month and the insurer will then pay out, up to a pre-agreed level, for any treatment that you have received. Private medical insurance can be expensive. However, if your ageing loved ones have the funds available, then it is an option that might be worth considering.

People can also look at having a health cash plan. Premiums for health cash plans cover the cost of expenses that are almost definitely likely to crop up. These are usually for routine treatments such as dental or optical care or even complementary therapies. With health cash plans people pay a small amount each month and then after they have received a treatment, send in the receipt to their plan provider for partial or full reimbursement, depending on the person's level of coverage.

If people decide to have expensive private treatment, then the reimbursement from their cash plan may be relatively insignificant. However, if people are receiving consultant services on an occasional basis or accessing complementary therapies, then the money received can be useful. Some health cash plans may also include add-ons such as life or personal accident cover or accidental death insurance.

If your ageing loved one has the funds available, then it is definitely worth considering what private medical coverage has to offer.

There are a large number and variety of insurance companies and insurance packages available, so it is definitely worth shopping around to track down the best deal. The internet is the best place to start as there are a number of insurance and cash plan price comparison websites that allow people to compare the premiums of different companies without having to contact companies individually. Note that some comparison websites only 'compare' selected insurance providers, so additional research is recommended to really save money. Also, if you are helping your ageing loved one to hunt around on the internet for the best deal, that can be a fun activity to share in its own right. If your ageing loved one has the funds available, then it is definitely worth considering what private medical coverage has to offer.

It can be a great help to have a health cash plan set up to help cover the cost of routine medical or health expenses that are

likely to pop up. By paying a little every month and then being reimbursed for part or all of a bill, people are easing the burden of paying for treatment that they are almost certain they will need in the future.

As always, people should seek the advice of professionals with reputable companies, be clear about what they are and aren't being covered for and (even though it can be boring) be sure to read the fine print!

For further information on health cash plans and private medical insurance and reputable service providers, please visit the Resources page on our website **www.ActionForAgeing.com**

Remember:

Although a topic in the book may not seem relevant to you and your loved ones today, it is worth reading because it may be useful in the future.

ACTION STEPS – Health care planning

1. Check with your ageing loved one if they are interested in or might already have a health cash plan or private medical insurance. ☐

2. If private medical insurance is not an option, perhaps they might be interested in a health cash plan? ☐

3. Seek information from professionals and cover from a reputable company.* ☐

4. By spending time together discussing a health care plan or hunting down the best deals on the internet, even if people decide not to take out a policy, it can be an enjoyable activity to share on a rainy afternoon. ☐

*Remind your loved ones to read the fine print.

TOPIC 26

Hearing loss

> **Fact:** Only one in three people who could benefit from an aid for hearing actually have one.
>
> **Fact:** That means 66% of people who could benefit from a hearing aid don't have one.

"Do I want my herring toasted? What herring?"

50% of everyone over 60 years old have some form of hearing difficulty.

At the same time, only one in three of the people who could benefit from hearing aids, has them.

Or, in other words, there's 66% of people walking around out there who could be helped by a hearing aid, yet don't have one.

Hearing can change over time, particularly as people get older. It is a good idea to check your hearing regularly. If your loved one has not checked their hearing in the last 12 months, then it's definitely a good idea to suggest it.

If they have been assessed by an audiologist and have been recommended an aid for hearing, if they still don't have one it may be worth asking them why.

Action on Hearing Loss (previously known as the RNID – Royal National Institute for Deaf People) has a hearing check available on their website: **www.actiononhearingloss.org.uk**

It's quick, simple and confidential and you can do it in the comfort of your own home.

There is also a telephone Hearing Check just call 0844 800 3838. (Calls from a BT landline cost up to 5p per minute. Other providers' charges may vary. Call set up charge may apply.)

If you wish to find out more information about deafness, hearing loss or tinnitus and the help and resources that are available call the Action on Hearing Loss help team for a friendly chat, telephone 0808 808 0123, textphone 0808 808 9000

Some people are concerned about the cost or feel daunted by the selection and technology. Others may be reluctant because they feel there might be some sort of stigma attached to wearing one. Everyone is different and we all have our reasons. Whether someone's reasons seem valid or not is entirely up to them to decide. However, if people feel strongly that the safety or wellbeing of their loved one is being impacted, it makes sense to express that.

The key word we keep in mind when discussing such subjects, is sensitivity. For some people, it might seem like a simple and easy solution to a problem, whilst for others it can have a far deeper and more profound impact.

With hearing aids, here are a few things to remember:

- People should have realistic expectations about what the hearing aid will be able to do, as they won't always make things perfectly clear.

- Understand that getting a hearing aid to perform at its best for your loved one is an ongoing activity requiring a subtle and methodical approach.

- Some hearing aids may sometimes whistle or squeak caused by 'feedback' and adjustments may need to be made to the earmould.

- Be patient and, especially with new hearing aids, don't give up. Try wearing them for a few days. It takes some time to get the best from hearing aids.
- Encourage your loved one to persevere until they find the right aid for them.

Carer Min

Hearing aids don't enjoy being under the shower and can be expensive to repair. A small, waterproof "hearing aid out?" sign above the bath tap as a reminder might just do the trick. Even if it works once, it saves big money.

Carer Min

I grew up with my Auntie Jess caring for me after my mother had died. Auntie Jess had developed boils in her ears when she was in her mid twenties, resulting in her hearing being severely impaired.

Her hearing aids were attached by two cords to a large battery case, roughly the size of a small mobile phone. The battery case had to be tucked into the top of her bra so that it remained out of sight.

Having her daughter, Alice and I to care for, Auntie Jess had her hands full and she developed the habit of turning her hearing aid off so that she didn't have to listen to our continual bickering.

Sometimes the bickering reached greater heights, resulting in our launching into full on assault mode where every pinch and

> *kick counted. Oh, how Alice and I loved giving our bodies a good workout in an all out brawl.*
>
> *Suddenly, Auntie Jess would come flying into the room, calling, "Children, children, stop fighting." I could never work out how she knew we were fighting if she was deaf. It finally dawned on me that she was picking up our vibrations through the floor boards.*

We don't recommend you wrestle with your siblings on the floor, but we do recommend that you try and think of some creative solutions to the challenges you and your loved ones face every day.

Using the vibration setting on mobile phones is a handy way to get a person's attention from another end of the house or end of the garden.

They don't need to answer, so it's as free as yelling out their name down the hallway.

Developing other communication skills like lipreading and sign language can be of immense benefit to someone with hearing loss

This may involve attending lessons and gathering information from books, the internet and whatever other resources you can get your hands on.

Action on Hearing Loss has a number of very helpful factsheets that offer tips on communication such as:

Tips when speaking to someone with hearing loss:

- Make sure you have the person's attention before you start speaking.
- Turn your face towards them so they can easily see your lip movements.

- Speak clearly, not too slowly, and use normal lip movements, facial expressions and gestures.

Tips if you have a hearing loss:

- Be open: tell the person you're speaking to that you have a hearing loss.

- Get a better view: stand a reasonable distance from the person so you can see their face and lips. Gestures and facial expressions will help you understand what they're saying.

- Play to your strengths: if your hearing is better in one ear, try turning that side towards the person speaking to you.

The full set of fact sheets and other helpful information can also be found at the Action on Hearing Loss website:

www.actiononhearingloss.org.uk/supporting-you

Carer Min

Auntie Jess used to take us to the cinema and in those days there were a couple of special hearing seats set aside. There was a special plug which Auntie Jess could somehow attach to her hearing aid thereby facilitating good hearing for the movie.

Invariably Auntie Jess' hearing aid would start squealing during the movie and we'd give her a nudge indicating that it was time to have a play with her hearing aids. These days, many cinemas have assistive listening equipment such as loop systems, so people with a hearing aid can choose to pick up the audio directly into their earpiece. Would have saved Auntie all sorts of bother!

In today's world, even though hearing aids are relatively state of the art, they still need looking after and tweaking.

Hearing aids have features such as t-coils that enable people to hear telephone callers or personal audio devices like radios and television more clearly, as well as audio transmitted via induction loops in public places (train stations, churches, theatres and conference halls).

Hearing aids can also have directional and omnidirectional microphones that enable the user to hear more clearly in given environments (directional for quieter one-to-one discussion, omnidirectional for at a restaurant table with friends). These microphones can be manually or in some cases automatically switched and activated.

Hearing aids generally come in styles that are behind the ear (BTE), in the ear (ITE) or where the aid is implanted deeper into the ear canal. The type of hearing aid will depend on considerations such as the level of hearing impairment, budget and personal preference.

Devices for the home to help living with hearing loss include telephones that have lights that flash when a call is incoming, vibrating alarm clocks, noise signallers (e.g. baby crying) and doorbell transmitters. Thankfully, technology is developing all of the time so that new devices to help people with hearing loss are becoming increasingly available. These, coupled with increased community awareness and improved planning and lawmaking that promote the interests and wellbeing of people with hearing loss are all positive steps, especially for our ageing loved ones for whom hearing loss is a frequent challenge.

If you want to find out more information about audiologists, hearing aid products and non-verbal communications, please visit the Resources page on our website: **www.ActionForAgeing.com/ Resources**

ACTION STEPS – Hearing loss

1. If your ageing loved one has not had a test in the last 12 months, suggest they take a hearing check or make an appointment with their GP. ☐

2. Have realistic expectations about the improvement to hearing. ☐

3. Encourage your loved one to be patient with their hearing aid – test it in a variety of environments and situations. ☐

4. Try having the hearing aid adjusted or try a different model– it's worth the little bit of extra time and effort ☐

5. Showers, baths, microwaves are not friends of hearing aids. ☐

6. Use simple communication tips such as making sure your lips can be seen and you are speaking clearly. ☐

Hoarding

> **Fact:** Once hoarding starts, it is very difficult to stop.

Nip hoarding in the bud

People don't just wake up one day and start stacking up piles of clothes, books, food containers, household items and rubbish throughout their house, so that within two weeks there is no way for anyone to get in the front door.

Hoarding is physically and emotionally very gradual. Only over a period of time, does someone's house move from being a little bit messy, to very messy, to being so messy that it becomes a danger to the person living there and those who have to enter.

It's good to be aware of what hoarding is and the risks it represents.

Prevention is better than cure.

> ### Carer Min
>
> *Over the years, I think I have become obsessed by hoarding too. Not to start hoarding, rather to clear the decks.*
>
> *Each person is an individual and as such, each has the right to say what stays and what goes. And, of course, to agree to a tidy-up in the first place. I have observed relatives become greatly frustrated because they want to remove clutter, but their loved one has dug in, usually stating that they'll do it themselves, when they get around to it. Which, when translated, means, "Never." Of course, that is up to them, but when the clutter becomes dangerous, that is when further action may need to be considered.*

As a family member or close friend, you are best placed to identify if your loved one is starting to show a tendency towards hoarding.

If they are, there is a lot to be said for trying to nip the habit in the bud. Once it takes hold, the heels get further dug in and, if it progresses, it can become a very real and major risk to health and your loved one's quality of life. The greater the hoard, the more traumatic and difficult it will be to resolve.

Everyone wants to keep treasured mementos and reminders of their past, but was the takeaway meal they had from the local Chinese restaurant on 4 March 1993 really such a big occasion that the sauce containers need to be kept? And the containers from the same restaurant a week later?

If such items are being held in the same esteem as the urn with Aunt Nellie's ashes, maybe it is time to review the situation.

Warning signs might be:

- Goods are stacked, piled or collecting in an inappropriate amount or location.

- Things are in plastic bags or groups of plastic bags that all look like they are being prepared to be taken somewhere (e.g. the charity shop, the rubbish bin or the garage) yet never move from their spot in the house.

- One or two plastic containers stacked on the kitchen bench are handy for when you want to store food. Having 30-40 stacked up, next to three feet of newspapers and 200 plastic bags jammed inside each other might be an early sign of hoarding.

The thing to also remember is that early stages of hoarding are often very tidy. Things will be nicely stacked, clothes or plastic containers will be spotlessly clean and while the old shopping bags might be full, they are standing symmetrically in line along the wall.

As the line between having stuff and the early stages of hoarding is a blurred one, often the best course of action is to encourage tidy housekeeping.

If your loved one has traditionally kept a tidy house, seeing bits and pieces building up where they never have on the floor or along the walls is something to be especially aware of.

Carer Min

In my experience, it has been mainly the family who take charge of tackling the hoarding issue. Carers such as myself, who are employed by care service providers, only occasionally become involved in clean ups.

One gorgeous little lady had absolutely no insight into the fact that her flat was virtually unfit to live in. Every week she did her shopping, insisting on purchasing enough food to feed four people.

Over a period of months and years, foodstuffs had fallen into decay. In the fridge. In the freezer. In the cupboards. In the corner vegetable container. When our service was introduced, at the request of a government body, our task was to restore the flat to a liveable state, being very careful not to in any way alarm or upset the lovely lady.

Two carers were appointed to conduct each visit. The decision to send in two carers at the same time was a master stroke. Frankly, one carer walking through the door and being confronted with such a gigantic task would have been overwhelmed.

We deployed a strategy of distraction and removal, executed with military precision. One carer would distract with conversation and queries at one end of her flat whilst the other would quietly remove the rubbish behind the rubbish, leaving the visible layer largely unchanged. Gradually we shifted the mountain of stuff, wrapper by wrapper, can by can, roller skate by roller skate (we wanted to ask, but couldn't) in a slow, unalarming way.

Some weeks later the unit was thoroughly cleaned and fully restored to order. And the lovely lady happily started hoarding a whole new range of treasures…

Carer Min

Many years ago I knew a person who lived alone and had become somewhat of a recluse. She would never allow anyone to enter the substantial home where she had lived for over fifty years.

When she passed away, family members entered the house and were amazed at what they witnessed. Accumulated in the kitchen were piles of old saucepans, toasters, baking ware and, to give you a mental picture, nineteen worn out kettles.

The rest of the house was likewise filled with items purchased over the years, discarded when they broke, but never removed.

A different person I know of was literally swimming over the top of clutter to move through their house. Breast stroke through the saucepans is certainly not the sort of exercise to be encouraged!!

Little research has been published on hoarding, but numbers that have been produced back up what Carer Min has experienced.

- In one study of older people who had been identified as hoarders, nearly 80% experienced substantial to severe inhibition of movement around their home.

- Furthermore, 70% of older hoarders were not able to use their sofa, dining chairs and table or other furniture because of obstructions and several had to sleep on a chair or on their couch because their beds were so piled with stuff.

- People who had never been married were more prolific hoarders, with more obstructions to movement around their house, than those who had been in long term marriages.

- The study also confirmed the biggest concern for all of us, that hoarding constituted a physical health threat for 81% of their hoarding loved one's and nearly half faced substantial (11%) or extreme (36%) threats to their wellbeing. That's why we all need to be very aware.

For full references and links to the study quoted above, please visit the Statistics page on our website: **www.ActionforAgeing.com/ Statistics**

If you do decide to remove the hoarded rubbish without your loved one's authority, it's best to do it very subtly and with great sensitivity. Where possible, consult their GP or the help line of an older person's charity for advice on how to manage things. Understandably, your loved one may argue passionately for each and every item to be retained. This can be very distressing so the more care and preparation that can be taken, the better the end result.

The ideal solution is to spot the early signs of hoarding and avoid the whole experience entirely.

Once again... Prevention is better than cure.

ACTION STEPS – Hoarding

1. Nip hoarding in the bud. ☐

2. Look out for when goods are stacked, piled or collecting in an inappropriate amount or location. ☐

3. Patience and subtle solutions rather than frustration-induced ultimatums are the best approach. ☐

4. Encourage a tidy house. ☐

5. Look to remove as much clutter as possible from their house. ☐

6. If your loved one stops letting you visit, it's a sign that you should definitely go. Their hoarding is likely to be in full bloom! ☐

TOPIC 28

Incontinence

Fact: Six million people in the UK have some degree of urinary or faecal incontinence.

Fact: 70% of those 6 million are women.

Fact: The average amount of time between a first experience of incontinence and seeking medical advice is six years.

Early ACTION is best

The sad fact is the NHS estimates that six million people in the UK have some degree of urinary or faecal incontinence, with 70% of those sufferers being women.

The more shocking fact is that the average length of time between a person's first experience of incontinence and seeking medical advice is....

Six years!!!! What!?!

Six years!?!

Urinary incontinence is where a mismatch occurs between the pressure of the bladder and urethra, such that the urethral pressure is lower than bladder pressure and an involuntary voiding of the bladder takes place.

For faecal incontinence, the intestinal muscles have been weakened (due to problems such as constipation) to the extent that the rectum can no longer close properly, thus resulting in involuntary stool loss.

Often, what starts out as a very occasional and very minor loss of control, which can be hidden with clothing choice or dealt with by tissue paper or some other self-made remedy, slowly evolves into a problem of incontinence that can no longer be managed at home. Typically, this is when the sufferer finally seeks medical help.

So, for an average of six years, people spend a great deal of time, energy and no doubt worry trying to sort out a way of dealing with the outcome of their evolving problem of incontinence.

Why wait until the problem is SO BAD, that it forces the person to seek medical advice? A common reason for the delay (sadly) is that there is still a lot of perceived stigma and shame attached to the topic of incontinence, so people do what they can to hide it and manage it themselves rather than seeking help from the start.

A large number of incontinence issues can be quickly and substantially helped or even fixed. Yet people are waiting six years until the problem is much more severe, before raising it with their doctor.

This six year delay is not good and we need to try and raise people's awareness that solutions to incontinence are available. And the sooner they are used, the better.

The subject is no doubt an awkward one for many people, but it is in everyone's interest to raise it as soon as possible.

If they don't have any issues now or haven't in the past, then make sure they know that potential solutions are readily available and that they ask for help immediately if/when an episode of incontinence happens in the future.

It's important for people to not wait for six years until the problem has become so severe that your loved one's quality of life has been very seriously, negatively impacted and the chances of remedying the problem have been reduced. The sooner incontinence is talked about openly, the better everyone's life will be.

Of the older people who are housebound:

- 53% are incontinent
- and that problem of incontinence is one of the major factors that led to the person being housebound in the first place.
- Beyond the direct issues of inconvenience and general embarrassment that surrounds incontinence, a person's need for frequent toileting and/or the urgency to void increases the risk of falls by 26% and bone fracture by as much as 34%.
- In short, a person's chances of being in a fall go up by 26% if they have incontinence (e.g. rushing to the toilet).
- How a person manages (or mismanages) their incontinence directly impacts on their safety in the home.

Reduced frequency
+ Reduced severity of incontinence

= less rushing around the house

= fewer falls

= a better life

= a happier and healthier loved one and family

The sooner your loved one seeks professional medical advice, the better!

The products available to help people deal with incontinence have improved substantially in both variety and effectiveness.

Compared to the ungainly pads and bags of yesteryear, there is a huge variety of products available today that are very effective and comfortable to wear.

There are disposable or washable alternatives for many products, such as:

- pull up pants
- waterproof underwear liners
- self adhesive or underlying pads
- bed and chair protectors
- colostomy bags

Across all the product ranges, there is a huge selection of choice between:

- whether they are for light, medium or heavy flow
- day time, indoors or outdoors
- night time and in bed

There are even plastic, portable urinals available for men and women, just in case nature calls and there isn't time to make it to the bathroom. The pull up pants in particular have made life so much easier for the wearer (and their carer too!). A great invention.

The high quality of today's incontinence aids also provide people with a sense of confidence, because they are visually unobtrusive and remain odour free if changed regularly.

It is critical that people's awareness of incontinence is raised and that people realise how important it is to be addressed at its earliest point.

The only way to get people to seek medical advice more quickly is to remove the stigma, and treat incontinence as the medical condition it nearly always is. For that, we all need to share relevant information as far and wide as possible.

It's as simple as that.

The challenge is, as always, how to get this message communicated and listened to, by the whole community. If YOU can help with that, that's fantastic. It's to ALL OUR benefit.

Remember: If a topic in the book doesn't seem relevant to you and your loved one TODAY, it is still worth reading it just in case it is part of your life tomorrow.

Where any type of incontinence has occurred, the most important first step is for your loved one to seek advice from their doctor.

The next step is to identify if they are eligible for any subsidised products or services. That information or a resource for that information should be sought directly from their doctor, as availability of goods, services and benefits will vary between areas and regions.

We also recommend you visit the website of Age UK for reliable advice and resources as well as quality products and services: **www.ageuk.org.uk**

A comprehensive list of resources for incontinence information, products and government services can be found on our main website Resources page: **www.ActionForAgeing.com/Resources**

ACTION STEPS – Incontinence

1. Look to raise awareness of incontinence amongst your loved ones and provide information and resources to them. ☐

2. Try to help prevent them waiting the average six years (!!) before seeking medical advice. ☐

3. Encourage people to nip it in the bud. ☐

4. Many types of incontinence can be quickly and easily remedied. ☐

5. Where there are potential issues, it is best to seek medical advice for diagnosis, what products might help and what help is available from the government/local authorities and various charities and organisations. ☐

6. Please help spread this information to as many people as possible. ☐

TOPIC 29

Inter-generational awareness

Inter-what...?

It's a clumsy sounding term but it simply means helping the younger generations understand and appreciate the older generations and vice-versa.

With the self-focused, technology driven world that the younger generation lives in and with the pace that lifestyles move, it can be very easy for them to assume that people of the older generations do not have much to offer or do not understand the world that the younger one operates in. This may have always been the case throughout history, but the feeling may be even stronger now, given the impact that technology has had on changing lifestyles. The world of people in their teens and 20's today is very different from that of their grandparents in many respects (but also very similar in others).

What's important to remember though, is that whilst there may be considerable differences in attitudes and lifestyles, there is still a tremendous amount that people of the older and younger generations can offer each other, in terms of knowledge, advice, support, understanding and help.

Younger people can contribute to the wellbeing of older people by:

Providing company – visiting, saying hello and having a chat

Practical help around the house, community or with a business – weeding the back garden, taking a pet to the vet or delivering a sculpture

Entertainment – singing karaoke (the worse the person sings, the better), reading the newspaper aloud, playing board games

Help with computers – showing the older person how to get online and the introducing them to the World Wide Web

Social activity – heading out for an afternoon of shopping, a sports event or trip to the movies

What it often comes down to, is Inclusion – by interacting with and involving the older generation in activities, the younger generation is helping to ensure the older generation feels included as part of society. Inclusion helps prevent loneliness and at the same time can promote positive physical and mental improvements to an older person's wellbeing.

Or in other words, older people can really benefit from being around and interacting with younger people. Not something that may come as a great shock, but sometimes it helps to be reminded of even the most obvious things.

The good news is, it's not all a one-way street.

Older people can contribute to the wellbeing of younger people by:

Providing practical information – how to bake a cake, how to change an electrical plug, how to play guitar, how not to put up wallpaper, how to speak Italian, how to save money on fuel bills, how to invest money in property, how to spend money on home furnishings and how to lose money on horseracing

Providing advice – tips for interviews or dealing with awkward bosses

Providing emotional support – providing an ear when a person may not be able to talk to their parents

Providing financial support – help with university fees, travel expenses, a new business

AND ONE MORE THING, WHILE YOU'RE IN BANGKOK BE CAREFUL OF THE LADIES IN PATPONG DISTRICT. THEY MAY NOT BE ALL THEY APPEAR TO BE!

Offering insights gained from years of experience – lifestyle choices, life lessons learned

Mentoring – helping a younger person with education, a life plan, along a career path

Spiritual support – with a lifetime of experience, older people may be able to provide help to a younger person who is interested in religion or spirituality

Human capital

Over a lifetime, people build up what is referred to as human capital (knowledge). Passing that information and experience onto younger people is extremely important.

Having spent years investing in and accumulating their human capital, this becomes a wonderful and valuable gift to hand on to the future generations. This doesn't only relate to huge things such as the secret process of cleaning a nuclear reactor without everyone blowing up or the spiritual wisdom gained from 60 years spent silently meditating in the monastery garden. Human capital relates to every form of information that a person has gained over their lifetime, that can be of benefit when passed onto others, to help improve their knowledge or understanding. Showing a young window-cleaner how not to fall off a ladder is an example of transferring human capital.

Carer Min

If your relationship with your loved one is a one-to-one type, then you may be privy to hearing the family history, which if it's not recorded by you right there and then, will likely be lost forever.

A very good tip once passed on to me – the shortest pencil is better than the longest memory.

That's right. You absolutely MUST write it down. Record it. Make a video. Set up camera, forget it's on and have a chat.

Do whatever it is you need to do to ensure that the stories, names, dates, places and relationships are all accurately captured for family members in the years and generations to come.

I utter those words emphatically. I cared for two older relatives who relayed a wealth of bygone family history and family members are now requesting information concerning the family, which I am unable to give them.

My memory has clogged up and I regret not writing everything down whilst I was listening to this fascinating history first hand because now I find I am unable to remember most of it.

> **A further tip:**
> Your ageing loved ones will likely have lots of family photos.
> A great idea is to write down the names, date and location on
> the back of the photos so that the people can be identified in
> years to come. This is particularly handy if a member of the
> family decides to trace their family tree.

Encouraging interaction between the generations is a really important action that people can take, to help with the wellbeing of people of all ages. Programs are being introduced every day to help promote this interaction, such as home share schemes where younger people without a home move into a spare bedroom of an older person who is living by themselves. The benefits are free or discounted accommodation in exchange for providing the company, security, help and many other benefits that people enjoy from living with another person. There are also programs such as younger learners of a foreign language spending time with older people who speak the language as their native tongue, so they can not only provide help with pronunciation and grammar but also provide insights into culture as well. This makes for a much richer learning experience for the younger person and provides wonderful social engagement and inclusion for the older person, resulting in improved self-esteem and overall wellbeing.

By encouraging people to get involved with other generations, we are looking to promote the wellbeing of everyone.

There are many associations and groups that provide ways for people of different generations to get together. If you wish to find out details of what programs and initiatives are on in your area or if you wish to see what is happening in other parts of the UK and world for inspiration, then please visit the Resources page of our website. **www.ActionForAgeing.com/Resources**

AGE Platform Europe

In the Resources section, you can also find links to AGE Platform Europe. AGE is a European network of 165 organisations of and for people who are 50+, which aims to provide a voice and promote the interests of senior citizens across Europe. AGE has 7 main policy areas: Anti-discrimination, Employment and Active Ageing, Social Inclusion, Social Protection, Health, Accessibility and Solidarity between Generations.

ACTION STEPS – Inter-generational awareness

1. Where possible, think about ways that you can encourage younger generations and older generations within your circle of family and friends, to have more interaction together. ☐

2. Remind the younger ones what they have to gain from enjoying time with older people. ☐

3. Remind your ageing loved ones what they have to gain from enjoying time with younger people. ☐

4. People should be encouraged to think of the increasingly large older population as representing an opportunity to society, rather than a burden. ☐

5. The more friendship, education, fun, advice, experiences, activities, appreciation and help the young and old can exchange between them, the better off we all are. ☐

TOPIC 30

Internet

Fact: 57% of people aged 55-74 use the internet very rarely or not at all.

The world at their fingertips.

That is what access to the internet represents. If someone says they aren't interested in the internet, it might be because they don't realise the endless opportunities and resources it has.

It's not just about reading the news and exchanging emails.

If you ageing loved is a Silver Surfer, one of the 43% of 55-74 year olds who use the internet frequently, then that's great. If your loved one is one of the 57% who do not use it at all (or very rarely), then it might be worth asking them why.

If someone doesn't want to use the internet on philosophical grounds ("the internet is a plague"), they feel that they have better things to do with their time ("I'd rather take a nap") or because they think it is a waste of money ("I rather spend £20 a month on beer"), then that is completely fair enough.

However... if someone would like to use the internet but does not, because they don't know what it is, how it works, what they need to do in order to get online or what to do once they are there, then perhaps there is an opportunity for yourself or your friends and family to pitch in and help.

So, if someone is not an internet user, the first thing to establish is why they aren't using it.

If they say they aren't interested because they don't see the thrill or benefit, then perhaps running through the below list may get a few good ideas going:

- They can do all their **supermarket shopping** and have it delivered to their front door when it suits them. The online supermarkets also remember what people bought last time, so that reduces the need for making or keeping long lists of the same stuff each week. If your loved ones enjoy the shopping experience, then maybe they can just get the heavy goods like laundry powder and their bottled and canned products delivered, to save them lugging them home. It's a much nicer shopping trip if their bag only has a loaf of bread and two light bulbs.

- Bidding at an **online auction** for rare hobby items that they would otherwise never find. Miniature 1870's porcelain thimble with a picture of Queen Victoria nude bathing, anyone?

- Looking at homes for sale or rent on **real estate websites** in case your loved one is planning to downsize or upsize. Or perhaps they want to get an investment property, check out what The Jones' next door are selling their place for or just want to see what £10 million will buy them in Manhattan or St Moritz these days.

- **Talking live via video** to their friends and relatives across the country and the world, anytime, for as long as they want – maybe even for free! They can be sitting in York and seeing their grandchildren who are living in Fiji, reading them a bedtime story or keeping them awake with terrible singing.

- Investigate the **family history** and gather a mind-boggling amount of publically available information from the various genealogy websites and public records offices. Discover exactly where Great Aunty Gertie lived in Coventry in 1897 (a disused coal mine – poor thing) and why Uncle Burt was dismissed from the Army during the First World War (for having a wonky moustache).

- Can read the **latest local newspapers** to find out the important news today in London, Tokyo, New York, Mumbai, Sydney, Beijing, Moscow, Tel Aviv, Casablanca, Durban, Sao Paulo and Milton Keynes.

- Can **watch video clips** that are educational on any topic imaginable (just in case they wondered how to perform heart surgery in a carpark with a coat hanger and bag of crisps) or see people reviewing different products (giving their opinion if the new golf clubs made from banana paper really do add 300 yards to your long game) or for simple entertainment (watching video of a cat swinging around on a ceiling fan).

- Pay income tax, car tax and submit the vast majority of other **official documents**. Nothing amusing about that, but instant submission online is better than filling in the forms on paper, remembering to post them and then hoping they reach the right department.

- Can **listen to radio** from around the world, **buy music**, read about their favourite performers, join forums and chat rooms, watch videos of concerts and interviews and even find out what the correct song lyrics are to songs they have been singing incorrectly for 50 years (but I thought they were singing "Stand by your van"?).

- Can look at and **share photos, video, news** of every place, animal, thing, whatever with people all over the world.

- Can **write a blog**, which is like an online diary, telling the world about their thoughts on politics, world peace, what is good or bad about society, if they think a movie star's eyebrows are a lot further apart than they used to be or whether they had peanut butter or honey on their toast this morning. Whatever topic they want to write about, there will probably be someone out there keen to read it and

they can read other people's blogs too

and exchange comments. "I think your blog about the length of your cat's whiskers was very insightful. It is no exaggeration to say it has changed my life."

- They can enjoy a couple of glasses of wine and still **travel around the globe** on their screen, without being pulled over by the police and arrested for surfing under the influence.

- They can look up what **old flames** look like on social networking sites.

- They can meet potential **new flames** on dating or social networking sites.

- What they had best avoid though, is having a few glasses of wine and then hitting the dating websites. Who knows what sort of trouble they may get themselves in!

- And contacting ex-partners whilst under the influence is to be absolutely avoided at all costs too. Waking up and finding that you had sent 147 messages to your first love (who was until last night happily married with four children in Aberdeen) is perhaps a good enough reason to stay off the internet altogether. Actually, no it's not. Instead suggest putting a little note up on the side of the computer screen — **RESIST THE URGE!**

- They can do the majority of their **banking and bill paying** without having to step outside or more importantly, not have to stand around in a bank queue watching a shop owner in front count out their coins in £100 piles.

- They can **bargain hunt** and purchase insurance, holidays, vacuum cleaners, toothpick holders, cars, boats, kitchens, books, DVDs, beekeeping gloves, football programs from the 1930's and every other sort of product imaginable. The only things they can't buy online are time and next week's lottery numbers. Although you can get things to save you time and there are people who are happy to tell you what next week's numbers are. Strangely, those people have not ever won the lottery themselves, which always seems a little odd.

- They can exchange **emails** with people or groups of people instantly and keep in touch with everyone, regardless of where in the world they move to. It's like having their own PO box in a post office in the sky, that they can receive mail into and send letters from. Unlike the local post office, sending email on the internet is free and open 24/7. If they want to send a physical package though, they will still need to pull out their wallet.

- They can find out about **job opportunities** locally and abroad, launching a new business or details on charities and organisations that they may like to **volunteer** with. It can be a new online business selling odd socks, or giving a few hours a week to helping sort paper at the local recycling depot or perhaps applying for the role of Secretary General with the United Nations. Well, if you don't ask you don't get.

- They can find **information on everything** from hobbies to health, spirituality to sport, Aardvarks to Zombies and whatever else that crosses their mind.

Carer Min:

Gerald, the brother of my beloved late husband Peter, is 80 years old and is a very keen silver surfer. He delivers a constant, daily stream of jokes, news articles, hilarious letters of complaint, cartoons and all sorts to his wide email group. The internet enables him to exchange photos of his grandchildren across the world with my sons who have children of their own. The Internet enables him to keep in touch with his army mates from 50 years ago. The Internet enables him to keep in daily contact with family and friends that span many years and now many miles. The Internet has given he and his lovely wife Dorothy a fantastic opportunity that they have successfully and wonderfully embraced. His brother's family (my two sons and I) are very grateful for this.

If there isn't anything on the preceding pages that sparks your loved one's interest, mention that these are just the tip of the iceberg.

If they feel they aren't interested because they are too old (nonsense), it's too expensive (computers and internet are available to use for free in many areas), it's dangerous for crime (so is walking down the street), they may accidentally break it or press the wrong keys and start World War 3 (unlikely unless they are Mr President and the key they are pressing is the big red one that has LAUNCH MISSILES written on it), they feel it's too complicated (there is plenty of help available and their 4yo grandchild seems to manage) then all of these issues can be overcome with a little help and patience from their friends, family or others in their community.

Some people are flat out not interested and that is completely fine.

If your loved one is potentially interested, then providing them with the help to get them online and enjoying all of the benefits that the internet has to offer, is a truly fantastic gift to provide.

Please visit our website Resources section, for more information on how people can access the internet for free and what training and help is available from various organisations and charities. **www.ActionForAgeing.com/Resources**

ACTION STEPS – Internet

1. If an ageing loved one is not an internet user, it may be helpful to try and find out why. ☐

2. Sometimes people are not aware of what the potential uses are, so providing them with some of the benefits that are listed may raise their level of interest. ☐

3. Computers and internet classes are available at the local library or charities. ☐

4. Helping older people onto the internet can unlock a hugely exciting and interesting doorway to the world of information and social activity that the person may not have ever imagined possible. ☐

TOPIC 31

Intimidation, fear & security

Fact: Young people are more likely to be the victim of crime than older people.

People can do terrible things!

In an ideal world, we would all live in peace and harmony and be trusting of our fellow man. But, unfortunately, not all of our fellow men are cut from the same moral cloth, so we must all be wary.

Or putting it another way, watch out for the baddies.

Carer Min

Many years ago I was asked to visit an older person living by herself in a unit situated within an extensive housing commission accommodation complex.

Over a period of weeks I couldn't help noticing that if she heard footsteps outside her front door she would become agitated.

One day I said to her, "Hetty, I can see that you become nervous when you hear footsteps, is there something wrong?"

Hetty indicated that she would get into trouble if she told me. I assured her that there was nothing she could have possibly done wrong and if there was a problem I might be able to help.

> "Well, every week I have to pay £20 security money to some young boys who live here. When they come for their money they tell me that if I tell anyone about it I will be bashed up."
>
> I was horrified and notified my boss who made enquiries with the police. The boss was told that the police knew the racket was going on, however, until one of the victims laid a formal complaint there was really nothing they could do.
>
> Sadly, this type of crime and the dilemma it creates between reporting the event and fear of retribution is not uncommon.

Unfortunately the problem faced by Hetty was not and is not a unique one. Whenever our loved ones are vulnerable, there will be heartless people out there to terrorise them, robbing them of their possessions, confidence and happiness.

What thieves and muggers rely on is that people's fear will keep them quiet and stop them from seeking help from the authorities.

A good way to try and reduce the likelihood of people being terrorised, is to encourage active and vocal communication and interaction amongst the neighbours.

Collectively, people have a better chance of standing up to and deterring those who might seek to intimidate and steal from them. However, that relies on a solid sense of community spirit.

A great way to build that community spirit and get people talking to and supporting one another, is via neighbourhood support groups.

- While Neighbourhood Watch encourages people to keep an eye out for strangers or burglars, a neighbourhood support group encourages people to meet regularly to discuss community issues that they all share.

- Starting a neighbourhood support group can be as simple as dropping a leaflet through your loved one's neighbour's door, inviting them to come along to an afternoon or evening with other neighbours to discuss local issues.

- Whether it is two neighbours, five or ten, it doesn't matter. It creates a way to communicate with neighbours and provides a forum for discussion, instead of simply saying "hello" as people pass each other on the street.

- A further benefit is that they allow for neighbours to get to know each other better and therefore they become more inclined to keep an eye out for others.

- If your loved one's neighbour knows that they are at home every day and they see bottles of milk outside uncollected, or rubbish building up in the front garden, they will be more likely to check on their safety.

- If they don't know anything about their neighbour, they might just assume they are at work or have gone on holiday.

The more people interact with their neighbours, the safer they'll all be. And the more ways that communication can be encouraged, the less risk there should be of crimes like extortion.

> ## Carer Min
>
> *One day when I went to visit a new client, he couldn't wait to tell me how he had been conned a few days previously. A young man had knocked on his door and sadly explained how his wife was ill, he was unable to work and the kids were starving.*
>
> *My client kindly gave him £200 and patted himself on the back for his fine gesture to a fellow man. Later on the same day he was speaking with a neighbour who told him that he had been visited by this nice young man who needed help. He had given the conman £100.*
>
> *So that made it £300. Not bad for 30 minutes work. And he probably won't be paying any tax on that either...*

Older people are vulnerable. We all need to do what we can to protect them.

Additional actions to encourage are:

- Have less money lying around their home. When a criminal knows that cash is likely to be available in easy to locate places and in sizeable quantities, they will have a motivation to break in.
- Keep windows and doors locked.
- Where possible, have security grills and doors installed.
- The easier it is for people to get in and out of houses, the more houses they will break into.
- Make criminals work for it!

For additional security, it can also help for your loved ones to have:

- An intruder alarm at the front door.
- A personal alarm on a fob around their neck, so that in the event that they feel in danger, they can raise an alarm for help.
- Stickers on windows for alarm companies. Even if an alarm is not installed, their house gives the appearance of extra security.
- A peephole in the door to allow them to see who is at the door before opening it.
- Good lighting at the front door and around the outside of their house or building.
- The more lit up a door, the less inclined thieves will be to use it.

Family members may know what needs to be done, but it can be difficult to put into practice, because people don't always have the awareness to be security conscious of their home and belongings, all of the time.

Some charities and local organisations offer help with funding and installing home security products such as door and window locks, front door spy holes, door chains and mirrors and door bars.

If you would like more information regarding security and safety products and services for older people, please refer to our Resources page on our website: **www.ActionForAgeing.com/Resources**

ACTION STEPS – Intimidation & security

1. Encourage your loved ones and their neighbours to form a community support scheme. ☐

2. Check with their neighbour that they are aware of your loved one's habits and timings, so that they are more likely to notice if anything is out of the ordinary. ☐

3. Encourage less money to be kept around the house. ☐

4. Where possible, have door and window locks and grills fitted. ☐

5. If funds allow, installing an intruder alarm is also very helpful. ☐

6. Discuss the advantages of wearing a personal alarm fob around their neck. ☐

7. Maybe put an Alarm Company sticker in their front window. ☐

8. Or a spy hole, door chain and mirrors for added protection? ☐

9. Ensure the doorways around the house are very well lit at night. ☐

10. Check if your loved one is eligible for free or subsidised security products and services from a charity, organisation or the State. ☐

Topic 32

Invisibility

Older people,
particularly those living
alone, can sometimes
feel almost invisible.
Loneliness and isolation
are terrible
problems that are quite common
amongst older people in the community. This is
a very sad situation and one that everyone can hopefully
help to rectify, over time. Ideally, it is good for people to be
aware of loneliness and isolation and try to encourage their
family, friends and neighbours to be as active as possible
in helping the older people around them avoid it.
This can be by simply keeping an eye out for older
neighbours who might seem to keep to themselves
or perhaps calling your own ageing parents, friends
or relatives to see how they are and what they are
up to. If they say "not much" then hopefully this
book will be able to provide a few ideas to
encourage a different   answer next time!

The easiest actions	people can
take are to smile	and say "Good
morning" to an	older person
as they pass	on the street.
This might still	be done
regularly in	some parts
of the	country but
certainly in	the cities
it is very	rare indeed.

For older people who may be experiencing loneliness or are also challenged with financial hardship, the charity Independent Age may be able to assist.

Independent Age is a unique charity, providing lifelong support to older people on very low incomes. They provide information and advice, practical help and emergency financial aid through their network of staff and dedicated volunteers across the UK and the Republic of Ireland

Just as importantly, they offer friendship and the chance to socialise to those who are lonely and isolated. Supported by Independent Age, thousands of older people are able to maintain their independence, contribute to their communities and enjoy a good quality of life, secure in the knowledge that their help lasts as long as they need it.

For more information please visit their website:
www.independentage.org or contact them via email:
charity@independentage.org or direct phone **020 7605 4200**.

ACTION STEP – Invisibility

1. Saying "Good morning" is a lovely way to acknowledge someone and makes both people feel good. ☐

TOPIC 33

Key locks

> **Fact:** Key locks cost between £15 and £25.
>
> **Fact:** They come in many varieties and are easy to fit.

Simple – possibly life saving

A key lock is a small metal box that stores the house key and when the cover is closed a number code has to be pressed to re-open the key lock. Key locks are normally installed somewhere close by the front door.

Key locks are recommended to be installed outside your loved one's home so that ambulance staff, family and trusted neighbours, can all gain access to the home in an emergency.

The code number can be stored at the local ambulance and fire station to facilitate prompt entry.

Key locks are quick, easy and cheap to install and they provide a possible life-saving service.

If your loved one has pressed their neck/wrist alarm and they are unable to move, it means that emergency services are able to gain immediate access.

If you would like further information on key locks or the contact details for a supplier, please visit the Resources page on our website: **www.ActionForAgeing.com/Resources**

ACTION STEPS – Key locks

1. Investigate which key lock is most suitable for your ageing loved ones. ☐

2. Provide them with information on the costs and benefits of a keylock. ☐

3. Help them to install a key lock outside their house. ☐

Kitchen safety

> **Fact:** People are more likely to have a fire start in their kitchen than anywhere else the house.
>
> **Fact:** People are more likely to be interested in fire safety tips after their kitchen has been on fire.

Accidents and injuries with older people frequently occur in the kitchen due to cooking flames, spillages, appliances being mishandled, items in cupboards falling or being difficult to reach or inappropriate things being zapped in the microwave. Whilst the variety of ways we can injure ourselves in the kitchen is almost endless, there are a few handy tips that can help minimise the dangers to ageing loved ones.

The first thing to consider is that the need for people to modify their behaviour, habits or their kitchen itself, is impacted by their cognitive and physical condition. How is their brain functioning at the moment and in the near future and how is their body strength, balance and reflexes? Some people remain sharp as a pin into their 90's whilst others may experience some form of dementia or physical deterioration from relatively early on.

I JUST THINK MAYBE IT'S TIME FOR A CHAT ABOUT HOME SAFETY

What's important is that people are aware of the fact that their ageing loved one's brain functioning and physical condition will change over time and that keeping an eye out for promoting safety around the house is an ongoing and evolving process. Indeed, suggesting once to people that they do X or Y for their own good may not reap the safety benefits hoped for. It may take a sustained effort, over many years if necessary, to try and gently encourage and coerce a loved one towards good kitchen habits that are for their long term improved wellbeing.

We can all be resistant to change, so it therefore helps if people can be as sensitive and respectful as possible when suggesting new patterns of kitchen behaviour be followed or new kitchen products used. Providing people with small aid items as unexpected gadget gifts might be more effective than cutting out pictures of products from a catalogue and sticking them up on the refrigerator door.

A sturdy step stool or set of night lights as a Happy Grans Day present are far more interesting and useful than another pack of tea towels or box of chocolates.

Some key kitchen safety tips for older people are:

- Keep the floor clear and free from coverings such as mats or rugs as they represent a risk of falls. The one mat that is a good idea for the kitchen though is a non-slip, water absorbent mat in front of the sink. That will help prevent any water splashed from the sink escalating from being a bit of a trouser-dampener up to a full-scale falls risk.
- When purchasing kitchen chairs, select models with arm rests so that older people can sit down and get up with greater ease.

- Avoid having loose power cords across worktops or looped on the floor. Even if they are in a location that they are unlikely to be tripped over directly, they may still catch onto a chair leg which in turn causes someone to lose their balance.

- Remove flammable liquids from the kitchen. Often people keep mentholated spirits and lighter fluid and all sorts of highly combustible stuff under the kitchen sink, which can either help cause a fire or act as a powerful accelerant. Away from the cooker it goes!

- Encourage the use of a timer when cooking food. Becoming distracted or forgetting completely about items being cooked represents a very real fire danger.

- Remind people to take pans off the flame/heat if they are called away to answer the phone or front door.

Carer Min

One afternoon I walked into the kitchen where a dear client had been making vegetable soup in a huge boiler. A complete bunch of celery stood upright in the centre of the pot, supported by unpeeled potatoes, tomatoes, carrots, etc. This had been cooked until the pot boiled dry and the celery stench permeated throughout the entire unit.

My client had absolutely no awareness at all about the soup, reassuring me that she was going to have the soup for dinner. I knew that what we were looking at was completely inedible. Therefore, my challenge for the day was to convince her that a tin of vegetable soup would be far tastier. We got there eventually, but only just!

- Install a dual smoke and monoxide alarm on the ceiling and put a fire extinguisher under the sink. Both can be bought online in two minutes, installed in less than five minutes and then be at the ready to save lives and property. Testing the alarm once a month helps ensure the unit is operating properly and it also gives the neighbours a good scare too. Help keep them on their toes!

- Step stools are very useful in helping people reach items that are high in the cupboard. They can also double as a clothes-horse to dry tea towels on

- Have a nightlight on in the kitchen. They cost as little as £10 for a pair and can plug into a standard electrical socket.

- Have favourite recipes copied and printed into LARGE font. If no photo copier is available, instead of writing out by hand, someone can take a picture with the camera on their mobile phone, email to themselves and print out the 'picture' on a high resolution printer. Yes, that definitely sounds like a good job for a teenager to do for their grandparents.

- Be aware of effects of medication at different times of day. Drowsiness whilst lying on the couch watching TV is great. Drowsiness whilst frying a big pot of chips is not.

- Whilst cooking, encourage people to wear short sleeved tops or those with tight fitting long sleeves to help reduce fire risk. Also, loose clothing is more likely to catch on something like a pan handle or door knob and cause someone to spill what they are carrying and possibly burn themselves. A skin tight, one-piece Lycra body suit would certainly provide an optimum level of safety to the wearer, however that may be outweighed by the heart attack risk for anyone who sees them wandering around in it.

- Consider having the garbage disposal unit disengaged.

- Keep appliances clean and free of grease and crumbs etc, as these can all contribute to an increased fire risk.
- Keep medications securely stored.
- Remind your loved ones about what is safe and what isn't safe to put in the microwave. Also, it is better to have microwaves on counters at waist height, as those that require people to bend over or stretch up will increase their risk of a fall, dizziness, spillage or burn.
- Remove appliances from the bench tops or make sure that the cords are securely positioned.
- Check the use-by date on cans of food in the cupboards and items in the furthest depths of the refrigerator and gently encourage your ageing loved one to let you dispose of them. Or if the food is really off, perhaps just open the rubbish bin lid and whistle loudly. The old food may rush across the floor and hop in the bin all by itself.
- Suggest moving tea towels or raising curtains that hang too close to the cooker.
- Suggest keeping frequently used heavy items, such as dinner plates and tinned food, at a waist level, easy-to-reach location to avoid the risks that bending down or reaching up high can present to older people.

34 – Kitchen safety

- Consider if modifications might be needed to allow for mobility aids in the future. For example, if your parent has difficulty walking now because of a dodgy hip, it might be worth looking at how their kitchen may need to be modified to allow for a walker or other mobility aid in a few years time. Rather than waiting until a walker is in use and needing to find the money and have the home modifications all done at the time, perhaps making gradual modifications is helpful?

For older people who might be in a stage of dementia, the approach to kitchen safety (and household) can be similar to that taken when child-proofing a home for toddlers. As an older person's brain functioning deteriorates, they might be more prone to doing things like trying to eat small household items like matches, plastic, erasers or washers

This 'older adult-proofing' may include having knobs on cookers removed or gas shut-off valves installed to help prevent unintentional ignition, having child-proof locks or latches on cupboards that contain items that could be dangerous or getting rid of the 'junk drawer' that contains all sorts of items like birthday candles or clothes pegs that can represent a choking risk for people with advanced forms of dementia.

Remember:

Many of the topics we discuss may seem extreme and irrelevant now, but it's good to read about them anyway because they may well be part of your reality tomorrow.

The important thing about trying to encourage any habit or home modification is that the views of your ageing loved ones need to be respected. This can be done with great sensitivity whilst also being firm, especially where someone's safety and wellbeing might be at risk and they might not be completely aware of this.

Such discussions are never easy or simple, as we are all resistant to change and an old habit is difficult to shake no matter how 'bad' it might be. But it is certainly always worth trying to be aware of how a home can be made safer and encouraging action where possible.

Prevention is better than cure.

Action speaks louder than words!

For more information about kitchen safety, quality safety/aid products and suppliers and a printable version of the Kitchen Safety List, please visit the Resources page on our website: **www.ActionForAgeing.com/Resources**

ACTION STEPS – Kitchen Safety

1. Review the kitchen safety tips in the list. □

2. Check if your ageing loved ones have any bad kitchen habits or a potentially hazardous kitchen set-up. □

3. Raise your concerns and discuss potential solutions. □

4. Maybe turn the monitoring of kitchen safety into a game, so it doesn't seem so much like you are pestering them about something that 'has been perfectly safe for years'. □

5. Help raise awareness that just because something has not caused an accident previously does not necessarily make it safe. □

6. Remind your ageing loved ones that we all change as we get older and that the more small actions we can take and small tweaks to our bad habits that we can make, the better chance we have of staying healthy, safe, independent and mobile for longer. □

7. Consider buying safety items and gadgets for making life easier as presents, as what greater gift can we give someone than improved wellbeing? □

8. When it comes to improving kitchen safety, action definitely speaks louder than words. □

Knitting & other activities

Fact: 4.5 million people in the UK have an interest in knitting/sewing.

Fact: The world's biggest knitted Christmas tree helped to raise £7,000 for the North Devon Hospice.

Fact: In excess of 700 knitters combined to knit the tree, using approximately 6,000 balls of wool and 1,400 knitting needles

Fact: The oldest tree knitter clocked in at 100 years old.

Now, where are those needles?

An important part of helping people live happier and healthier lives is to take action to encourage them to stay involved in activities they enjoy.

Some people require no help and are living as busy a life in their seventies and eighties as they were in the earlier years, but a considerable number slowly withdraw from being involved in clubs and associations or from personal hobbies because of factors such as declining health and reduced income.

This is very natural and to be expected. Sad, but true.

However, what you can take action on is to:

- recognise your loved one's possible decrease in energy or finances
- help identify activities that they will be capable of for years to come.

- help them action any hobbies they used to have or create curiosity or enthusiasm for a new one
- help them develop their skills and provide a lot of encouragement

Many people will have been knitters, once upon a time. As they've aged and perhaps as arthritis has set in, they may have discarded the knitting needles, because they're no longer able or motivated to complete large projects. The skill will not have been lost and many may simply need a little encouragement to pick up the needles once again.

Suggesting smaller items such as baby booties for a new grandchild or great grandchild might be a good start. Certainly not as daunting as a King Size bed cover in any case!

Carer Min

In my personal experience, I have persuaded groups of people (friends and neighbours) to all knit small squares, so as to bring them all together to form beautiful patchwork quilts and knee rugs, some of which were donated to charity.

Asking one of them to embark on an individual project such as knitting a pullover or throw rug may seem intimidating or involve too much of a commitment, while suggesting that they produce a small square as part of a group effort will more likely appeal on many levels.

It's amazing to observe how quickly small squares are knitted with such confidence, because the needles and wool feel so comfortable to use once the older person has them back in their hands again.

The steps to encouraging YOUR loved one depend on what they want to participate in. But if you apply the principle of encouraging them in their hobbies, then the outcome will hopefully be the same: a happier, more fulfilled life.

For knitting:

- If you know or can find other loved ones who are knitters and live nearby, maybe consider inviting two or three of them to come to the house for a knitting session and a cuppa?

- Knitting is a great occupation to undertake because the participants are able to have a chat whilst the needles are clicking, so this activity provides a great opportunity for people to communicate in a relaxed manner.

Carer Min

The pride which emanates from people when they set out pieces for a patchwork rug on a large table, and then juggle them around until they are satisfied every square is in its right place, is almost indescribable.

The squares are then sewn together with wool. And if you know an older person who can crochet, they can create a beautiful border around the edges of the rug.

On the days when the rugs are finally completed and displayed for inspection, the people are usually already talking about the next one they will make.

(For knitting specification aficionados, the squares normally knitted are 80 stitches to begin and 50 rows. A nice size for mature fingers to handle!)

Whilst the hobby we've talked about here is knitting, the underlying principle is the same for all activities. Hobbies provide your loved one with:

- entertainment
- exercise of the body and/or brain
- a way to meet people
- an activity to focus on
- a sense of achievement
- a motivation to keep active and healthy
- a way to make inexpensive gifts for their grandkids

Why not take action today to help with your loved one's happiness tomorrow?

If you would like more information and suggestions about activities **www.ActionForAgeing.com/Resources**

ACTION STEPS – Activities – knitting

1. Recognise that your loved one is changing. ☐

2. Identify what activities they can continue to do. ☐

3. Encourage them to start or restart their hobbies. ☐

4. Help them develop their hobby, maybe with the use of the internet to search for information or groups of people who share their interest. ☐

5. Encourage them to maintain their activities. ☐

6. Where possible encourage your loved ones to be involved in group activities too. ☐

TOPIC 36

Medication

Fact: A pill tray with seven days and morning, noon, evening and bedtime compartments costs £3 and is very handy.

Fact: If your loved one's prescription is free on the NHS they can get their pill mix delivered in a blister pack for free.

Blister packs – very handy

Everyone has their own preference for how they manage their medication and how they take it.

One way of organising the daily or weekly intake of tablet style medication is in a blister pack.

The blister pack has provision for storing medication seven days a week with morning, lunch, dinner and bedtime medication packed into the appropriate time slots.

Blister packs can cater for many types of oral medications that people have been prescribed by the doctor.

From the carer's perspective, blister packs provide an improved means of supervising a medication regime without anyone having to juggle multiple tablet containers.

The big advantage of blister packs is that it is easy to identify whether the medication is being taken, or whether the person needs to be prompted to take their medication by their carer.

- If your loved one gets their prescription free on the NHS then they can get their prescription mix put into a blister pack for free.

Carer Min

Some people will tell you that they always remember to take their medication and it doesn't need to be in a blister pack.

Frankly, they can tell me all day about how good their memory is, but I never take a chance because my memory is not what it used to be so even if they remember what tablet they are up to, I won't.

A little tip when prompting someone to take their medication – remain with them and observe them actually swallow their pills. Because as people age, they may accidentally drop their medication instead of it going in their mouth.

Also, some mischievous types might just be pretending to take their medication. There's always one!!

There are a number of products on the market to assist in reminding people when to take their medication and what to take.

These include:

- alarms that can be set at the required medication intervals
- little plastic tray pill organisers
- reminders that can be arranged by telecare providers and sent via a text
- message or some other electronic or telephonic means
- automated pill dispensers that can provide the required set of medication at particular intervals

As with anything to do with medication, we strongly recommend that people seek advice from their doctor to find out what medication assistance products might be of benefit, now or in the future.

Also, it is helpful if you can monitor your loved one's behaviour over time. With problems like dementia, their ability to keep track of their medication intake may wane slowly over time. Whilst a product such as a pill dispenser may not be required now, it might be needed in the near future.

It's also worth keeping an eye out for useful new products that may be of help. For example, for people who might be at particular risk of a heart attack, a product that is a tremendous idea is a small plastic box that they can wear on their neck chain that contains two chewable soluble aspirin.

- For an at-risk person, having an aspirin readily available at a second's notice can potentially be a lifesaver. Aspirin is a very effective way to shorten the time for an anti-platelet effect to begin, thus helping to prevent a blood clot from worsening.

- If your loved one has a chewable, soluble aspirin on them already, then they may be able to self-administer or indicate for someone first on the scene to do so.

- The alternative of carrying an aspirin in their pocket or wallet is not a particularly good one. Aspirin tablets are prone to crumbling, especially when even the slightest moisture is absorbed.

At the risk of being repetitive, for all advice regarding your loved one's health and medication, we would strongly recommend you seek information from their doctor.

Carer Min

Some carers may be called upon to administer eye drops. Generally speaking, eye drops have a suggested use-by date of thirty days after opening. To save carers having to remember when they were opened, simply write the date on the outside of the eye drop box.

If you would like to find out more about various medication products and services, then please visit the Resources page on our website: **www.ActionForAgeing.com/Resources**

Remember:

Many of the topics we discuss may seem extreme and irrelevant now, but it's good to read about them anyway because they may well be part of your reality tomorrow.

ACTION STEPS – Medication

1. Seek medical advice on appropriate pill dispensing options. ☐

2. If possible, monitor your loved ones taking their medication. If you have any concerns about your loved ones regularly taking their medication, it is worth checking. Better safe than sorry! ☐

3. If heart attacks are a risk, consider buying an aspirin dispenser. ☐

4. Encourage your loved one to make sure that their medication-taking is as safe and as easy as possible. ☐

5. Always seek medical advice first. ☐

Message in a Bottle

To Do List:

1. Obtain MIAB kit. ☐

2. Write personal health details on the MIAB form. ☐

3. Stick the form in the small plastic MIAB bottle. Include a recent photo. ☐

4. Put the bottle in the compartment door of the refrigerator. ☐

5. Put MIAB sticker on the outside of the refrigerator door. ☐

6. Put a MIAB sticker up inside the home front door. ☐

A fantastic program across the UK is the Message in a Bottle scheme. This isn't about burnt-edged treasure maps being washed ashore in a glass bottle having been thrown over-board by a drunken pirate in 1763. It is much better and more important than that.

DID YOU PUT YOUR LEFT OVER STEW IN MY EMERGENCY DETAILS AGAIN, GEORGE?

The Message in a Bottle is a free program whereby your loved one fills in their health details (medications, ailments, allergies, etc) and rolls it up, sticks it in a small plastic bottle and puts it in their refrigerator.

They then put a small sticker of a green cross on their refrigerator and inside their front door. If they have an accident, the sticker on the front door or refrigerator will indicate there is a bottle in the fridge that can provide the emergency services with the information they may require, in the event that your ageing loved one cannot give them the answers.

The forms, bottles, and stickers are available free from associations such as Lions Club International who understand how important having accurate and quick information can be in an emergency situation.

Please help raise awareness of the Message in a Bottle program by telling all of your friends and family about it.

It is free, quick and possibly life saving!

For information on who to contact for your free forms, stickers and bottle, please visit the UK website of Lions Club International **www.lionsmd105.org/Community/MIAB** or call their UK phoneline **0845 833 9502** (Mon-Fri 8.30am-5.00pm)

ACTION STEPS – Message in a Bottle

1. Let your ageing loved ones know about Message in a Bottle. ☐

2. Encourage them to contact a local provider for the bottle, form and stickers. ☐

3. Spread the word about the program so that more people know about it. ☐

Moisturising cream

Fact: Moisturising cream costs £5 for a 300g bottle.

Fact: And it will help your loved one feel like a million pounds!

Use it

Daily application of moisturising cream to the skin tends to create a soft, smooth and supple skin.

This is very helpful for older people, as they have sometimes developed quite dry, scaly, skin, especially on their arms and legs.

Most importantly, keeping people's skin soft and moisturised also helps protect them from skin tears.

Carer Min

I find that when I am in shopping centres, airports and other areas where there are large numbers of people, I will automatically glance down at older people's skin to check their hands, arms and legs, to see if they've been using moisturising cream on a regular basis.

They probably think I am some strange, nosey-parker who might be about to pickpocket them, but I'm afraid I can't help but look!

The reason this is a special tip all on its own is because it's usually the carers who make the time to moisturise people's legs and arms and can reach their back, because as people age they tend to do a quick job or completely forget to do it altogether.

The use of emollient creams is often recommended by health care professionals.

- Emollients act as a moisturiser, a type of skin cream that covers the outer layer of the skin (epidermis) with a thin, protective film that helps reduce loss of moisture from the skin.

There is a huge variety of emollients available, with some especially formulated to also assist with medical conditions such as psoriasis or eczema.

If you would like more information about moisturising and emollient cream, and the contact details for specialist suppliers of moisturiser for people of all ages, please visit the Resources page on our website: **www.ActionForAgeing.com/Resources**

ACTION STEPS – Moisturising Cream

1. Encourage loved ones to use it because it feels good and keeps their skin fresh. ☐

2. Keeping skin moist and supple also helps prevent skin tears. ☐

Nails – fingers & toes

> **Fact:** Older people frequently suffer ingrown finger and toe nails.
>
> **Fact:** Nail deformation can be a side effect of medication.

Take great care

Come the day when your loved one needs assistance in cutting their nails, it might be you, as their nearest and dearest, who will be asked.

In taking action, you need to be aware of some of the dangers involved, and what can be done to make it easier and safer.

The first thing you will notice with an older person's finger and toe nails is that they can be extremely tough and brittle. Some tips to keep in mind:

- Before the clippers come out, soften the nails by soaking your loved one's toes/fingers in warm water for a few minutes.

- This has the added benefit of feeling very nice and soothing. And if there is some music on in the background and lavender oil in a small dish, even more so!!

- When cutting their nails, be they fingers or feet, it is important to be very careful not to cut the skin. Even the slightest wound to an ageing loved one can become seriously infected.

- If your loved one has diabetes and the wound doesn't heal, then this simple cut could potentially result in them having their toe, foot, hand or even the limb amputated.

Carer Min

When I did my formal care training many years ago, we were forbidden to ever cut a client's toenails for fear of an injury or infection.

Whenever a person (who is a client rather than a family member) has asked me to cut their toe nails, I have always politely refused and have organised a podiatrist to visit them.

Many podiatrists will do home visits and usually charge a pensioner rate.

The importance of sticking to this policy was affirmed for me when I once visited someone whose foot had become infected after he'd made a cut in his toe.

His toe became fly blown resulting in maggots developing and when I met him his entire foot was encased in bandages. And if it didn't heal properly, then surgery and likely amputation loomed.

The last time I saw him he was in good spirits and feeling optimistic about keeping his limb. I never did find out how he finally fared, as his carer service was moved to another team and I lost track of his progress.

I shake my head when I think of these little toe and finger digits and how, despite being so small, they can be the source of real havoc.

Always ensure that any injury is properly treated.

If you are unsure about what proper treatment is, then please seek professional medical advice.

Prevention is better than cure.

For information about resources and products for grooming and care activities, please visit the Resources page on our website: **www.ActionForAgeing.com/Resources**

ACTION STEPS – Nail Cutting

1. Be very careful when using nail clippers on your loved ones. ☐

2. Recommend they soak their hands/feet in warm water to soften the nails. ☐

3. If a cut does occur, ensure the wound is properly treated and seek medical advice where appropriate. ☐

4. If the infection is not correctly treated, limbs can be lost! ☐

TOPIC 40

Nutrition

> **Fact:** For those over 70 years of age, the recommended daily nutritional intake is 1,200–1,600 calories from wholegrain foods, a variety of coloured fruits and vegetables, low fat dairy products, lean meats, fish and poultry and eight glasses of fluid.

Food matters

The importance of nutrition to the health and welfare of your loved one cannot be overstated.

Eating food, and the right sort of food, is absolutely critical for their wellbeing:

- it helps with their strength in performing daily tasks
- it helps with their energy level
- it helps with their immune system
- it helps with their alertness and mental faculties
- it helps to keep them regular

No surprises there. Especially with the last one!

What you may not have considered though, is that good nutrition has a major impact on fall prevention and recovery.

If your loved one maintains a healthy body and they slip:

- they will be more likely to have the mental alertness and reflexes to catch hold of a hand rail or some other fitting
- and they will have the strength to catch themselves and stop them from falling

If your healthy-eating loved one does fall over:

- they will have stronger bones to handle the impact
- they will have a reasonable amount of flesh on their leg and hip bones to help absorb the impact
- they will have upper arm strength to help absorb the impact
- their internal organs will be sturdier to handle the impact
- their body's capacity for recovery will be better
- their immunity to infection will be stronger

As older people are not as active as they used to be, the volume of food they need to eat may be less than when they were younger. However, the importance of maintaining a good, balanced diet remains.

This means that they should be encouraged to eat a variety of food for all the minerals and vitamins that bodies require and, where possible, keep the intake of saturated fats to an appropriate level. What is an appropriate level of fat intake varies from person to person and depends on factors such as their weight, appetite, medical conditions, age, level of frailty and daily activity levels.

For older people the key considerations are:

Fibre – Keeps the tummy area healthy and bowels nice and regular. Not a pretty subject but for some people daily movements or lack thereof can become one of the main topics of concern (and even conversation!). This means eating fruit, veggies and cereals that are high in fibre.

Fluid – Regular and frequent intake of fluids such as water, juice, milk, tea and coffee are important. As our bodies age our kidneys don't work as well as they once did and a lack of fluids can result in dehydration. Also, some older people are not as

sensitive to noticing their thirst so they may not take in fluids even when their body is desperate.

Vitamin C – Maintaining a healthy body requires Vitamin C. Sometimes people may suffer from a lack of Vitamin C because they have sensitive or weak teeth and have difficulty eating the sort of crunchy fresh fruit and veggies that are rich in Vitamin C.

Sugar – Sugar is important for energy levels or for those who may be underweight and need to gain some calories. For people who are overweight, their intake of sugar should be limited. This is not rocket-science, nor ground-breaking news. But it is important.

> **Carer Min**
>
> *Older people can sometimes be incapable of preparing their own meals or they might be physically able but have lost interest in doing so. Therefore, they may rely on Meals on Wheels or food provided by carers such as friends and family.*
>
> *When visiting your loved one, why not bring meals from home, where possible? Maybe prepare extra servings when you are cooking/baking and place them into takeaway containers and name and date them, so that they can be stored in the older person's freezer.*
>
> *Left to their own devices I have found that many of the older people tend to eat very little if they are living by themselves.*

Vitamin D and calcium – From the age of thirty, our bones start the process of calcium depletion. As we get older, the process speeds up. To help combat the loss, it's often recommended that Vitamin D supplements are taken and that people eat calcium rich foods such as dairy and milk products and Vitamin D rich foods such as cereals, oily fish and spreads. The best source of Vitamin D is direct sunlight, so that's another reason why you should encourage your loved ones to get out and about at regular intervals.

Zinc and iron – People need zinc to help bolster their immunity system and aid recovery from injuries, whilst iron helps blood and circulation and helps prevent anaemia. Zinc can be sourced from meat, breads and shellfish, while iron can be sourced from red meat, leafy green veggies, dried fruit and cereals.

The above is a quick guide to the key nutritional elements that apply to people as they get older.

The best action for people to take is to make sure their loved one speaks with their doctor or health advisor and receives complete nutritional advice applicable specifically to them.

Every person is different and therefore has different nutritional needs.

Snacks

Older people may find that their capacity to eat regular sized servings at breakfast, lunch and dinner may not be as it once was. A good action to take is to encourage them to have healthy and nutritious snacks between meals.

These snacks can take the form of:

Spaghetti, sardines, salmon, well-cooked eggs or beans on toast.

Yogurt, soup, breakfast cereals, crackers with jam or cheese, fruit, plain cake, fruit cake, digestive biscuits and oatcakes.

Bread rolls or sandwiches in a variety of grains, with tinned fish, cooked meats or cheese, bolstered with condiments such as sauces and relishes.

What can have an impact on your loved one's nutritional intake?

It is good to be AWARE of the reasons outlined below explaining why some people's nutritional intake might be at risk, and, if possible, to rectify the problem to ensure they are maintaining a balanced and nutritious diet.

Some causes of malnutrition to be aware of:

- not wanting to walk to the shops because of sore feet, ill-fitting shoes, deterioration of eyesight, safety or incontinence
- being unable to carry shopping, open tins of food or unscrew jar tops because of a lack of strength
- being concerned about spending money
- being unable or fearful of driving to shops.
- being concerned about availability, cost or safety of public transport
- the closure of local shops and fear of travelling to an unfamiliar place
- lack of motivation to cook
- tiredness or loss of appetite as a side-effect of medication
- forgetting to eat
- Oral problems such as mouth ulcers or ill-fitting dentures making eating food a painful experience

By being aware of the above, it can help you and your ageing loved ones to keep an eye out and take action to help avoid potential malnutrition issues or nip them in the bud early.

We strongly recommend if you or your loved ones have any questions regarding nutrition, that the advice of a doctor be sought.

Carer Min

Whilst working one weekend I was scheduled to visit two older clients and ensure their Meals on Wheels had arrived. I arrived at the first client at 3.15 pm (when I was rostered to be there). He ate a spoonful of his meal and then announced he would have the rest of it for his tea. I urged him to have some more while it was hot, but he wouldn't budge. I then told him I'd put it in the refrigerator, because he had an ant problem.

I then moved on to my next client, who was also very happy to receive his meal but promptly placed it in his refrigerator, promising that he would eat it at dinner time.

The following day when I did my rounds, where did I find the meals? Still in both of the refrigerators. Oh dear.

Good nutrition is CRITICAL for people's health and well being.

It's therefore CRITICAL that we keep a regular check on what, how much and how often our loved ones are eating.

Remember: Although your loved one may have always been a healthy eater, that doesn't mean they necessarily always will be.

There are many reasons why a loved one may not be getting the nutrition they need and it is important that people recognise this and take action when needed.

Action for food shopping/preparation may take the form of:

- delivering shopping items to your loved one yourself or arranging for a neighbour to do it.

- picking up and driving your loved one to the shops once a week.

- organising online grocery shopping on their behalf, so that the shopping is delivered to their door at a specific time.

- buying them an electric can opener.

- calling at dinner time and checking what they have eaten.

- checking if they have any ailments that prevent them from shopping, preparing their meals or eating.

- arranging for a meals home delivery service to drop off meals.

- checking the contents of their refrigerator and making sure that any old food that's out of date is removed.

- setting an alarm clock in the kitchen to go off at 7pm each day with a large note attached saying, "prepare dinner now."

- preparing a shopping list and meal timetable for the week covering breakfast, lunch and dinner (which ensures they eat a balanced diet and that they have the required ingredients)

The above is to raise awareness only and is not to be taken as advice.

People should seek the advice of a doctor for specific nutrition and health recommendations. In short, it's important for people to take action to help their loved ones:

- eat the right food, at the right time, in the right quantity.

- seek professional medical advice on nutrition and ACTION it.

If you would like information or additional resources with respect to nutrition, meal preparation or home delivery services, please visit the Resources page on our website: **www.ActionForAgeing.com/ Resources**

ACTION STEPS – Nutrition

1. Gather information about nutrition and older people. ☐

2. Inform your loved ones why nutrition is important. ☐

3. A great exercise can be to suggest they record what they eat for the week. Write it down. ☐

4. Then they can take the list to their doctor and seek advice on their nutrition. ☐

5. Maybe arrange to deliver the shopping yourself, via a neighbour or the internet. ☐

6. Enquire if your loved one has any ailments preventing food preparation. ☐

7. Check to see if your loved one may prefer meals from a home-delivery service. ☐

8. If so, perhaps you can help investigate costs and funding options. ☐

9. Buy them an electric can opener, a jar top opener and whatever other gadgets you can find to help make food preparation easier. ☐

10. Call your loved one at meal times to check what they are having. ☐

11. If they have started becoming forgetful about mealtimes perhaps setting an alarm for 7pm in their kitchen, with a note saying "eat dinner". ☐

12. Help them prepare a shopping list and meal timetable each week. ☐

13. Encourage nutritious snacks if their appetite at main meals is low. ☐

14. Where possible and with great sensitivity to their dignity, try to ensure they are not missing meals for financial reasons. ☐

TOPIC 41

Outings

Fact: 20% of older people can't remember the last time they did any exercise.

Fact: Only 44% of older people are aware that certain exercises prevent falls.

As your loved ones age, it is good to encourage them to continue taking walks and enjoying outings as frequently as possible.

For older people particularly, getting out and about can be of benefit:

- to help keep their body active
- to help keep their mind active
- to help keep them socially active
- being active helps reduce the risk of falling over
- maintaining good health helps them maintain their independence

Sometimes, ageing loved ones may prefer staying at home, because of personal issues such as mobility or incontinence.

Where someone is not faced with such a challenge but is simply no longer in the habit of daytime excursions, then a little persuasion or perseverance may pay big rewards with everyone's wellbeing.

The word 'persevere' in this sense can mean offering reasons why a short drive might be enjoyable and perhaps light bribery of a nice lunch at a café.

Perseverance does not mean dragging your loved one by their feet down the front stairs and slinging them into the boot of the car 'for their own good'.

Once agreement has been reached, in that they agree to venture out with you, it's good to make sure that:

- their footwear is comfortable
- that you have the appropriate walking stick, walker or wheelchair on board. Perhaps hire one for a special day trip or weekend?
- and do a triple check that all the necessary medications are with you too
- if they regularly take certain items on an excursion, write a list and keep it at the door

Simply heading to a beach or canal, up into the mountains, or to a local park or heath and enjoying a cappuccino sitting in the car, can provide a nice change.

Once in a nice location, you can enjoy all sorts of activities:

- take a walk
- take some photos
- have a picnic
- draw the landscape

- read a book
- go for a swim
- do some knitting
- play cards

If your loved one is housebound for much of the time, they will really appreciate the chance to get out and about with you, regardless of what is planned. Sharing time and enjoying each others company is wonderful for wellbeing.

If you can fit in some exercise along the way, that is ideal.

It's also worth being aware to:

- not plan too many activities
- not arrange too many time dependent commitments
- keep your day out as simple and commitment free as possible

That means much less stress for you and less stress again for your ageing loved one.

Carer Min

Shopping centres and high streets provide plenty of stimulation and also an opportunity to enjoy an inexpensive meal, particularly if your loved one's appetite has faded over a period of time.

Fish and chips seem to be at the top of the list and personally I find it quite interesting to note that people's appetite suddenly increases when on a day out. It might be all that fresh air – or the promise of not having to wash any dishes.

Because of the time taken and distance covered, the outing to the shopping centre or high street may result in your loved one becoming tired long before you are.

So remember to factor in a few sit downs throughout the day, at cafés for a drink or a park bench, which provide a good chance for resting, refreshments and people watching.

For the housebound, people watching at the seaside or in a park makes a refreshing change from the view they usually get from their living room sofa.

Carer Min

Outings are great for your loved one and can make a refreshing change for yourself.

It's funny how easy it is to get lazy and succumb to the easy repetition of daily housebound life, when it can be reinvigorated with a simple five minute drive down the road.

If you would like more information about activities to enjoy with your loved one, please visit the Resources page of our website: **www.ActionForAgeing.com/Resources**

ACTION STEPS – Outings

1. Aim to encourage your ageing loved one to be out and about at least three times a week. ☐

2. Where people require specific items for an outing, maybe keep a checklist by the front door that can help. e.g. medication, glasses, special shoes, etc. ☐

3. Change what activities you do each time, e.g. taking photos, playing cards or reading a book. ☐

4. Include exercise at every opportunity. ☐

5. Don't plan too much. ☐

6. Do plan multiple toilet stops, tea breaks and rest time. ☐

Pendant & wrist alarms

> **Fact:** A life saving pendant alarm costs £10-20 per month.
>
> **Fact:** A medium size pizza from up the road costs £15.

Make sure they are worn

Wrist and pendant alarms are a wonderful invention in that if your loved one falls or is unable to access the phone for some reason, all they need do is press the button.

The wrist alarm looks like a watch whilst the pendant alarm hangs from a string around the neck. Both have a button that activates an alarm when pressed.

Within seconds:

- An operator will be talking with them via their alarm and asking questions to establish what assistance they require. Or if the alarm provides just an alert to the operator, then the operator will immediately send out an instant emergency notification to your loved one's contact list and/or emergency services.

- The operator will also be able to confirm that the alarm notification has been received and acknowledged by the contact or emergency services.

The specific alarm process that is activated depends on the type of alarm service employed, but the basic result is the same.

If your loved one is in trouble and has pressed the alarm button, then help will be on the way immediately.

The latest neck and wrist alarms are designed to be worn twenty-four hours a day and are both shock resistant and waterproof.

Carer Min

I have encountered people who absolutely insist on leaving these alarms beside the bed, on the kitchen table or in their walker basket. They believe that if they need assistance, they'll be able to get to it in an emergency.

That is completely nuts!

We all tend to believe that we're invincible, until the day we find ourselves in trouble.

When people do have a fall and their alarm is at the other end of the house, they ask themselves, "What was I thinking?"

And that question is asked every single day. People need to actively and relentlessly encourage their ageing loved ones to wear their neck or wrist alarm at all times.

It is utterly mad to do anything but that, as the alarms really do save lives.

To find out more about the services available in your loved one's area, it is best to consult their local doctor or health care provider.

Also, depending on circumstances and eligibility, funding for telecare products such as pendant or wrist alarms may be available from your loved one's healthcare provider or various charities and organisations. We recommend you visit the website of Age UK for advice and resources as well as quality products and services. **www.ageuk.org.uk**

For a huge amount of information and resources regarding personal alarms and other telecare products, please visit the Resources page on our website: **www.ActionForAgeing.com/ Resources**

Remember:

Many of the topics we discuss may seem extreme and irrelevant now, but it's good to read about them anyway because they may well be part of your reality tomorrow.

ACTION STEPS – Neck & wrist alarms

1. Seek advice from a local doctor or health care professional on what alarms and other telecare products are available. ☐

2. Help determine which alarms are most suitable for your ageing loved one. ☐

3. Discuss the options of renting vs purchasing. ☐

4. Encourage you loved one to wear their alarm, not leave it on a table. ☐

TOPIC 43

Pets

> **Fact:** Older dog owners spend an average 1.5 hours more outdoors every day than their non-dog owning neighbours.

Those who can, SHOULD.

Most people have had a pet of some description during their life and know the pleasure they can bring.

Dog, cat, bird, rat, fish, pig… you name it. It doesn't matter what the animal is, so long as the person likes the pet and the pet likes the person (although that can be hard to assess with goldfish).

So if your ageing loved one does not currently have a pet, it may be a good time to take action:

- find out if they are interested in having a pet
- if they say "no", perhaps provide information on all the benefits in case they haven't necessarily given them full consideration
- if they don't fancy a regular domestic animal such as a dog or cat, gather information on different pets
- encourage them to have a pet

The journal of the American Geriatrics Society has identified in various studies (medical proof!!) that older people who have pets are less stressed, have lower blood pressure and are more active than their non-pet owning peers.

Loneliness is a key problem for many older people, as a result of:

- lack of regular interaction with people
- sense of worthlessness
- lack of motivation
- lack of confidence

All of these can lead to a sense of an increasing level of social isolation.

They might feel anxious and that nobody is interested in them, or that people are judging how they look or what level of perceived success they may or may not have had.

These feelings are very common amongst older people, even those who might seem quite happy or relaxed when you have a brief interaction with them as a stranger or even on an ongoing basis as a family member or old friend.

Along with non-threatening companionship, the below are further good reasons why people might consider sharing their home with a pet, where at all possible.

Animals provide:

- affection
- entertainment
- interaction
- a sense of purpose
- occasional mischief
- a sense of reliance and responsibility
- love and loyalty

A dog will provide the above every minute of the day, whilst cats are a little fussier and tend to decide what mood they'll be in, on a wait-and-see basis.

One day cats almost attach themselves to their owner. Another day they are unable to be located, completely ignoring the "Here kitty, kitty, where are you?" calls. There is an old saying "Dogs have owners. Cats have slaves." Very true indeed!

But few people will deny the lovely flood of calm that washes over you when a cat is curled up on your lap, purring.

A pet will provide your loved one with endless entertainment and a sense of purpose and responsibility. In being relied upon to feed, clean, groom, walk or even clean up after a pet, people may remain active for many more years than they would have been otherwise.

- The Journal of Personality and Social Issues noted that older dog owners spent an average 1.5 hours more outdoors every day than their non-dog owning neighbours.

Older people walking their dogs are three times more likely to engage in communication with other dog walkers than people are if just walking through the park by themselves.

A different study of older people found that 75% of men and 67% of women considered their dog to be their closest friend.

Can you imagine how much more lonely all of those people would have been, if they didn't have a dog?

Obviously, when discussing a pet with an ageing loved one, serious consideration must be given for what the requirements of the animal will be and what your loved one is currently and is likely to soon be capable of handling.

Pets are supposed to be and generally are, a great source of pleasure and stress reduction. But if an inappropriate pet is selected, then the completely reverse result can occur.

When discussing pet suitability it is worth remembering:

- exercise level
- attention required
- food and health care costs
- grooming demands
- physical size

And don't forget to consider the life expectancy of the animal and what its alternative living arrangements will be, should anything happen to your loved one.

These may all seem to be obvious points, but sometimes, in the excitement of the moment, people may forget to consider one, two or all of them. Remember, the boa constrictor from the Amazon often looks smaller in the photos than in real life, and sourcing meals for 11 live chickens and a goat each day can be a challenge for a city-dwelling older person.

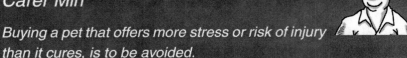

Carer Min

Buying a pet that offers more stress or risk of injury than it cures, is to be avoided.

This happened to one of my clients, who was devastated when his dog, Sam, passed away.

His family were desperate to find him a replacement friend and thought they could curb his grief by purchasing him a pet bird.

I arrived a couple of days later to encounter my client, aged 91, down on his hands and knees trying to entice his bird from under a bedroom cupboard.

Why did you let the bird out of the cage? "I thought he might like to have a look at the rest of the house and now I can't catch him."

Indeed. I wasn't as athletic as my client or the bird, so after a few, "Here birdie birdies," I departed with the full knowledge that he would catch that bird one way or the other. He already had a handful of feathers, so it was only a matter of time…

A week or so later my client asked his family to remove the bird because it was too stressful. I think a new little Jack Russell pooch has since moved in and is now running the house, much as Sam used to.

And without question, older people will always remember to feed their pet, whilst forgetting to feed themselves.

The benefits of a pet are:

- pets help increase people's happiness, by providing and receiving affection and giving them a sense of responsibility and purpose

- pets help reduce stress, blood pressure and anxiety with their simple, calming influence
- pets are sources of endless entertainment and relatively cheap entertainment at that
- pets don't judge their owner, or make them feel uncomfortable
- pets are a fantastic way to reduce loneliness and isolation

Great danes are lovely looking puppies with hilarious big, floppy feet, but…

So the simple action message is:

Encourage your ageing loved ones to consider having a pet (of some sort!!).

If you would like to find out more information about what pets are suitable for different living arrangements, please visit the Resources page on our website: **www.ActionForAgeing.com/ Resources**

ACTION STEPS – Pets

1. Check if your loved one is willing to have a pet. ☐

2. Help them identify what pets might be suitable. ☐

3. Gather information on their favourite pets. ☐

4. Join in the discussion of which pet to choose. ☐

5. If can involve all the family in the pet information gathering and decision, it can be a fun activity to share. ☐

6. Pets do make great presents (but best not have it as a surprise!) ☐

TOPIC 44

Power of Attorney & Wills

Fact: What is the percentage of people over 65 who have a Will and Power of Attorney prepared? Not enough.

Fact: What is the price of having them prepared? The price may be less than people may think. The cost of not having them can be much, much more.

It is very, very important that everyone finds out what Power of Attorney means and how it might be applied to their circumstances and carefully considers the potential costs and benefits.

A basic definition of Power of Attorney is the authorisation to represent someone or act on their behalf in business, legal or personal matters. The power can only be authorised whilst the person granting it is still capable of understanding what they are doing. If someone is too senile to understand the implications, then they can't sign over Power of Attorney to a relative or trusted person. It's too late. Power of Attorney can be general or specific to performing a particular task (e.g. selling a house) or they can be 'lasting' (or termed something similar to mean 'forever') which gives authorisation to act on another's behalf when that person is incapable of understanding what is going on and making their own decisions.

Put simply, if someone arranges for Lasting Power of Attorney to be given to their daughter and years later they were to suffer dementia and lose the capacity to conduct their own affairs, then their daughter would be able to assume control of her parent's personal, business and legal affairs (or whatever was identified in the document).

For the latest legal definitions and specifics on Power of Attorney for the country you live in, please visit the Resources page on our website – **www.ActionForAgeing.com/Resources**

Carer Min

One daughter I greatly admire surrendered her employment and independence in order to live with her father and care for him. Years later she was still taking care of him in his own home, a resolution which would not have occurred if his daughter hadn't set aside her own life and made such an incredible commitment. Holding Lasting Power of Attorney meant that the daughter was able to provide or arrange any service or equipment her father required.

On the flip side...

A mother gave her daughter Power of Attorney, after which being signed the mother rarely saw her. One day the daughter arrived and said she had something new to show her at her home. Upon arrival the daughter led the mother through the house out onto a timber deck which straddled a new swimming pool. Knowing her daughter and son-in-law's modest financial situation the mother asked, "Who paid for this?" "You did" was the daughter's reply.

Power of Attorney can obviously be very helpful in the terrible circumstance that a loved one loses the capacity to handle their own affairs. Where complications can arise is when a family member, acquaintance or friend is given Power of Attorney that is disputed by others. Some may feel a vulnerable person has been tricked or manipulated or that the person exercising Power of Attorney is doing so irresponsibly. The horror stories are

numerous and universally experienced across the world. This is why it is very important for people who have ageing loved ones to check if a Lasting Power of Attorney is in place or at least on the radar for consideration.

The cost of having a Power of Attorney prepared should not be measured by price alone, as the cost of not having one can be truly dreadful for all concerned.

The reasons why having a Power of Attorney is important are:

- the person gets to choose who they wish to have in charge of their personal affairs

- if something happens and the person becomes incapable, then their selected person is able to assume control relatively quickly

- if they don't have one in place, it may result in some or all of their funds being spent in legal fees to determine who should be in charge of their affairs

- at the time when someone becomes incapacitated, the stress on the family and friends can be incredible, because of legal problems or delays, financial constraints or sometimes (sadly) due to fighting between family members who might be wrestling for control of their family member's assets and affairs

Power of Attorney can be legally revoked, however the stress caused to the ageing person and their loved ones cannot be calculated.

Having a Will is also very important.

If people die and they don't have a Will, then the State is responsible for directing who gets possession of their assets. This means that their family, friends or charities and organisations that they may wish to have left their assets to, may get nothing or have to go through a lot of red tape and delays in order to get anything.

It's also important to note that unless someone is married or in a legally recognised civil partnership, then their partner may not necessarily be automatically entitled to anything. It doesn't matter if they have been co-habiting and their partner has been putting up with their snoring for 20 years, unless people have a Will formally written, their loved one's entitlement may not be recognised.

The best thing to do is seek advice from a solicitor or bank manager on having a Will drawn up that meets all the legal requirements. People can write their own, but run the risk of not doing it correctly. Which renders the document void and the intended beneficiaries being left with nothing.

Losing a loved one is a terribly stressful situation. Having to also sort out their muddled financial affairs whilst coping with everything else can significantly add to the trauma. Throw into the mix family member, ex-partners or some other person that the deceased couldn't stand the sight of, receiving an inheritance because in the absence of a Will, the State has had to distribute the assets as per the law.

Wills can be prepared for relatively small sum (£100-200) and can make a huge difference when it matters most. Where people do have a Will already, it is also important that it is updated if there are any significant changes in their personal financial situation or key relationships.

Power of Attorney and Wills are two things that people should definitely look at doing.

Based on the horror stories of many people, there are reasonable grounds for Wills and Power of Attorney to be made compulsory by law. But that is another discussion for a later time.

If you wish to get more information on Wills and Power of Attorney, some reputable service providers and also read about some real-world examples of why having a Power of Attorney in place is so very, very, very important, please visit the Resources section of our website **www.ActionForAgeing.com/Resources**

We also recommend you visit the website of Age UK for reliable advice and resources as well as quality products and services. **www.ageuk.org.uk**

ACTION STEPS – Power of Attorney & Wills

1. Check what Power of Attorney and Wills mean and where they may be locally available. ☐

2. Suggest to your loved ones they may wish to consider the benefits. ☐

3. A good reminder for all: Some simple actions up front can save people and their loved ones a huge amount of hassle and grief later. ☐

Let's not forget – Funeral Plans!!

Some people may wish to take out a funeral plan so as to ensure that the arrangements are made according to personal wishes and the costs of a funeral are met. The specific items covered will depend on the policy taken out, so it is important to research and identify the plan and provider most suitable for particular needs and circumstances.

The benefits of a funeral plan are:

- Peace of mind that some or all of the cost of a funeral will be covered by the policy so that this does not become a burden for someone else to pay.

- Particular wishes, such as a cremation or burial service can be arranged in advance.

- Funeral plans can be tailored to individual needs, to also include preferences such as particular readings or hymns, newspaper notices, floral arrangements or even a dress code.

- Comfort can be had knowing that funeral arrangements are taken care of so that the friends and relatives of the deceased are not required to make decisions at what can be a difficult time.

- The cost of a funeral varies widely between type, location and the 'extras' (such as who performs the service, type and number of vehicles, etc) but even the most basic of services is currently around £2,000-£3,000 and quickly climbs above that amount.

- For more information on funeral plans and reputable funeral plan providers, please visit our website Resources page: **www.ActionForAgeing.com/resources**

TOPIC 45

Shopping list

Fact: Shopping whilst hungry will cost you lots of money.

Make it once – use it forever

Most people will make their shopping list each week and it will contain:

- the same meat, fruit and vegetables as last week
- the same cleaning products as last week
- the same household items as last week

This means your loved one needs to write their list each week and remember to add items or if you are helping with organising their shopping, you may arrive and need to figure out what they usually have and what they need.

So we recommend you:

- create a blank weekly shopping list
- and photocopy it
- and keep it in your loved one's kitchen

That way, they can just tick the box of what they need and if they want something that is not on the list, then add it to the bottom.

The benefits of a pre-made shopping list are:

- it saves time and effort writing out the same things every week
- the list can have big fonts so it is clear and easy to read
- no one is hunting around for little, random bits of paper with this week's items on it

- the list can remind you what's needed if your loved one has forgotten to tick something
- it can be kept in the same spot on the kitchen bench or stuck up on the fridge

Please Note:

- a great brain exercise for your ageing loved one is for them to memorise their shopping list before they head off to the shops. They can then test themselves on their memory when they are in the store and use the shopping list in their back pocket/ handbag as back-up.

Carer Min

I have prepared a shopping list for all carers (workers, relatives and friends) who do shopping for their clients or family and friends.

It contains foods which people enjoy and, more importantly, food they can survive on that is readily available and inexpensive.

When I was working for a local carer service, I took my shopping list prototype in to the boss, who raved about it, distributed a copy to all of the carers for their input and then having updated it, printed it off.

Since then, I have been into the homes of people linked to that care service and sure enough, have seen those shopping lists on the kitchen counters and what's more, they're being used!!

A useful sized paper for the shopping list is A4 size, because anything above A4 is too big to carry around a supermarket.

The pre-written shopping list can simply have items ticked during the week, which means that come shopping time all the carer has to do is a quick check for any items that have been ticked and they're ready to go.

How many millions of people have someone who does their shopping for them, as well as those who do their own shopping but have short term memory loss? Plenty is the quick answer.

And studies have shown that people who use lists in supermarkets spend less than those who don't have a list.

Carer Min

When shopping, I work on the theory that if it's not written down on a list, the odds are I will forget it. Except for a nice bottle of wine. I never forget that!

An example shopping list is as follows:

SHOPPING LIST

BREAKFAST

Bread

☐ White ☐ Wholemeal ☐ Grain
☐ Raisin ☐ Rye

Cereal

☐ Bran Flakes ☐ Muesli ☐ Porridge

Eggs ☐ 1/2 dozen ☐ 1 dozen

☐ Butter ☐ Margarine
☐ Bacon
☐ Crumpets

Spreads

☐ Marmalade ☐ Apricot jam ☐ Peanut butter

LUNCH/DINNER

☐ Turkey fillets ☐ Chicken fillets
☐ Steak ☐ Sausages (freeze individually)
☐ Crumbed cutlets _____
☐ Cold meats _____
☐ Pasta salad
☐ Cheese (block) ☐ Cheddar ☐ Brie
☐ Other _____
☐ Ice cream

For a complete shopping list template that you can download and print out, please visit the Resources page on our website: **www.ActionForAgeing.com/Resources**

ACTION STEPS – Shopping list

1. Sit down with your loved one and write out a shopping list. ☐

2. Use that to create a shopping list template in a big font. ☐

3. Print lots of copies on A4 sized paper. ☐

4. Stick up the shopping list in your loved one's kitchen. ☐

5. Encourage them to use it!! ☐

Singing

> **Fact:** Percentage of people who can frown and sing at the same time = 0%

Even the shyest person will usually enjoy a sing-along and a great development in the world of activities for older people is the local song club.

Unlike singing groups and choral associations where the singing ability of the participants is of premium importance, the local song clubs for older people are focused on providing the opportunity for people to gather for the social enjoyment of singing in its own right.

Local song clubs are usually based in a community centre setting, with an experienced organiser, a couple of volunteers (often from a local choral society) and a musician.

The music and program will change from one club to another, however they will generally use music and

songs that are familiar to the group's members. They then look to make the songs more challenging and fun by adding layers to the music or having members play drums or other instruments.

The objective isn't musical perfection and a Christmas No.1 album (although some groups may have their own individual goals and dreams). Instead, what song clubs achieve very successfully is an increase in the personal wellbeing of their members. The singers have fun and meet new people who share their current circumstances. They can feel a boost in confidence and a reduced sense of isolation, and forge new friendships with local people.

Carer Min

I attended a singing group where the oldest singer was a 94-year-old gentleman. He was a member of another group who regularly visited hostels and nursing homes. There is no age limit when it comes to singing simply for the love of it.

I recall purchasing a plastic coated Rogers and Hammerstein song book years ago, and I and my songbook would spend hours under the shower together. The good news was that my aunt was totally deaf so I was in no way causing her discomfort and there were no water shortages in those days. Today, if I hear the tune of one of those songs, I'm 'off again', in full throttle.

Yes. Singing is good for the soul.

An idea for the family: how about digging out a CD of your favourite songs and printing off the lyrics from the internet. Invite the family for dinner and then present them with song sheets. It has all the makings of a great evening.

Alternatively, karaoke CD's are available and provide hours of entertainment.

This simple form of entertainment can be organised by just one person. You could well be the instigator of an ongoing family tradition.

From the perspective of improving overall physical wellbeing, the benefits of singing include:

• improved body movement and mobility

• improved breathing and blood flow

• better co-ordination

• improved brain reserves (as singers need to switch on the grey cells to remember lyrics and to play musical instruments)

If your ageing loved one is looking for a new activity that is local, social, fun, easy, inexpensive, beneficial in 101 ways and available in a friendly environment, then joining a local singing club may be just the thing for them.

For a comprehensive list of the major song club groups across the country and their contact details, please visit the Resources section on our website: **www.ActionForAgeing.com/Resources**

ACTION STEPS – Singing

1. Share the list of benefits of singing with your ageing loved ones. ☐

2. Find out if they are interested in joining a local group. ☐

3. If so, you can help them investigate where the closest are located. ☐

4. It's always good to encourage attendance to activities even as a trial, as quite often people can have more fun and in different ways than they may have originally expected. ☐

Skin tears

> **Fact:** 80% of all skin tears happen to the hands and forearms.
>
> **Fact:** Studies have shown that 85% of people whose care plans included specific interventions to reduce skin tears (including moisturising arms and legs twice a day) showed a decrease in skin tear incidence.

Older peoples' skin = tissue paper

Skin tears with older people tend to occur on the hands, forearms and lower legs, caused by brushing alongside any protruding surface.

In fact, UK studies have put the figure at 80% of ALL skin tears occurring to hands and forearms. Crikey!

Let's face it. There are hundreds of ways in which skin tears can occur to a person around their home that never posed a risk to their younger skin:

- doorway edges
- cupboard corners
- table legs
- car doors
- kitchen drawers
- shower doors
- on and on it goes…

When their limb meets with a sharp object their skin can be so fragile that it simply peels back, not unlike the lid when opening a tin of sardines.

This is why it's important for people to take action and reduce the frequency of skin tears by their loved ones in their home.

When a skin tear does take place, contact their doctor or a health care professional for advice, as all care needs to be taken to ensure that the wound does not become infected.

It is unrealistic to head to the doctors for every minor scratch, but it is critical that people are very aware of the dangers that infection represents to older people. If they don't feel an injury is worth a visit to the doctor, it's critical that they are very thorough in dressing the wound and monitoring its state.

Some examples of taking action around the home to help prevent skin tears are:

- If the shower door has sharp edges where the metal bands finish, try attaching a few layers of masking tape to cover the offending sharp edge.
- If the small drawer on the washing machine (for detergent) has a sharp corner exposed when the drawer is pulled out, it may help if the sharp edges and corners are filed down. Most are made of plastic, so the sharpness can be quickly and easily rounded.

These ARE NOT intended to be huge home modifications and they won't make anyone bulletproof.

These are simple, one minute jobs that should help to reduce the frequency of injury.

- With the pots and pans cupboard, many people have their cookware stacked higgledy-piggledy. This means that when someone with fragile skin reaches in to pull out a saucepan, they may well scrape the back of their hand against the tip of the frying pan handle.
- Also, often there is very little light or visibility inside the cupboard when people reach in, making them susceptible to getting their skin scrapped and torn on a sharp edge they can't see.

Potential solution:

Maybe it is time to change where things are kept in the kitchen?

Can the most frequently used cooking items be moved to a central, easily accessed place that doesn't require bending down and reaching into unlit cupboards?

When you have younger skin, these injuries won't even be on your radar. A scrape that happens to younger skin may barely result in a scratch, whilst the same event for an older person might result in skin being torn and blood flying in all directions. Not good.

People can also help keep loved one's skin healthy and supple by reducing the use of soap or detergent, particularly on the skin tear hotspots (hands and forearms).

Instead of soap, the use of emollient soap substitutes, emollient creams, ointments and/or bath oils is usually what is recommended by health care professionals.

- Emollients act as a moisturiser, a type of skin cream that covers the outer layer of the skin (epidermis) with a thin, protective film that helps reduce loss of moisture from the skin.

There is a huge variety of emollients available, with some especially formulated to also assist with medical conditions such as psoriasis or eczema.

When your loved one is visiting their doctor, remind them to ask about emollients and any recommendations that can be made.

> Skin tear prevention is much better (easier, healthier, cheaper and less painful!) than skin tear cure.

If you would like to use a checklist that will help you to identify potential skin tear hotspots around your loved one's home, or if you would like more information on emollients or skin tear first aid, please visit the Resource page on our website: **www.ActionForAgeing.com/Resources**

We strongly recommend that people seek advice from a doctor or healthcare professional when a skin tear occurs.

> ## Remember:
>
> Many of the topics we discuss may seem extreme and irrelevant now, but it's good to read about them anyway because they may well be part of your reality tomorrow.

ACTION STEPS – Skin tears

1. Print a copy of the skin tear hotspot checklist. ☐

2. Suggest your loved one reviews hotspots around their home. ☐

3. Looking for ways to reduce the number of sharp edges in the home can be a fun activity for the whole family. ☐

4. Encourage your friends to do the same for their loved ones. ☐

Topic 48

Swimming

> **Fact:** It costs around £3.00 to swim at a local pool.
>
> **Fact:** Seniors can get a six month pass for £100.

Swimming is a fantastic form of exercise and people don't need a pool in their backyard or an ocean on their doorstep to do it. Given the weather in the UK is not often described as 'tropical' and most of the year the temperature of the sea water along the rugged British coastline would freeze the nipples off a walrus, the availability of lots of heated, indoor public pools up and down the land is a very good thing indeed.

The benefits of swimming, particularly for our ageing loved ones are:

- it uses nearly all major muscle-groups so gives people's bodies an all-over workout
- it improves their cardio-vascular system (heart and circulation)
- increases endurance
- builds strength (which is good for fall prevention!)
- improves flexibility (also good for falls prevention!)
- improves posture
- has a low risk of injury because there is no stress on bones, joints and connective tissue
- is safer than other forms of exercise in public areas such as cycling, jogging and gym
- is free from potential hazards like other people, equipment failure and pollution

- public pools always have trained staff who are close by in case of an emergency
- relaxing, because it forces a regular breathing pattern and increases oxygen flow to muscles
- great way to rehabilitate after an injury
- can feel more like a fun leisure time activity than a hard workout
- a regular routine may help reduce high blood pressure, which lowers the risk of stroke and heart disease
- soothes the discomfort of back ailments and swollen joints
- it is cheap. No expensive equipment required. A pair of goggles and a cap can be bought for £10.
- the benefits to health and wellbeing can be gained whether people are a beginner or ex-Olympic champion
- when people have done enough, they can stop and get out of the pool. If they are on a bike, walking or jogging, they may be miles away from home.
- can be done alone or with a friend as a swim partner
- can be done in a class for social side and to improve technique
- games and sports in the water can be enjoyed whilst also being good exercise
- swimming is a lot more fun and better for people than sitting around watching TV

That is a long list of benefits. It is not a complete list, but in the interests of keeping things moving, that's probably enough for now.

Carer Min

Many of the older people I have encountered over the years who are regular swimmers have been those who were referred to hydrotherapy after their release from hospital. Hydrotherapy is conducted in warm water which makes the difference and its benefits (especially in improving wellbeing) are almost instant.

As they have thoroughly enjoyed going swimming again, some after a lapse of 60 years, many are keen to continue attending classes even after their bodies have 'healed'.

The strokes that are best for health and fitness are freestyle, backstroke and breaststroke. Experts recommend that for older beginners, the initial length of swimming should be kept to between 12-20 minutes. As people develop their technique and their body gets used to it, then they can look to gradually increase their times and widen the variety of their pace and stroke styles.

Additional benefits on top of the huge list earlier (just a few more, can't miss these):

By using different swimming strokes, people can change the muscle sets that are being exercised.

Helps avoid procrastination. If using a public pool, people are restricted by opening hours, which means that they have to plan ahead when they want to do exercise during the week. Making a commitment (even if only mental) that they shall swim on Mon, Weds and Sat morning is much better than having people think "I'll see how I go during the week" and then not doing anything at all.

People can safely test their limits and extend their swim whilst staying in the same, supervised place (the pool).

IF IT WAS GOOD ENOUGH IN 1905 IT'S GOOD ENOUGH NOW!

If they are meeting a swimming partner or joining a class or sports team, then it is harder for them to not show up. Who wants to be known as Larry Letdown?

It's also important to remind your loved ones that swimming for exercise is not just about doing lengths of a pool. People can enjoy water aerobics classes, exercises standing in the water or holding onto the side of the pool, water sports such as water polo, water badminton, synchronised swimming or diving (if it's safe and they know what they are doing – all lawyers please note: we aren't recommending 90yo first-time swimmers to be trying triple back-flips off the 10 metre tower).

As with all fitness activity, swimming requires consistent, regular action to be of most benefit. What's more, it usually feels more like a fun leisure time activity than an exercise workout.

For more information on swimming pool locations and resources on swimming training, programs and activities, please visit the Resources page on our website **www.ActionForAgeing.com/ resources**

ACTION STEPS – Swimming

1. Look for swimming pools located near your ageing loved one either on the internet or by visiting the Resources page on our website. ☐

2. Find out if your loved one is interested in swimming. ☐

3. Give them our fantastic list of the benefits of swimming. ☐

4. Check out the local pool cost and hours of swimming. ☐

5. See what classes are offered. ☐

6. Encourage your loved one to try swimming and go along at least twice, even dragging a friend along with them if necessary. ☐

7. Remind them that not only is it a fantastic form of exercise, it is great fun too! ☐

Technology/Telecare

> **Fact:** Currently, 1.75 million people in the UK actively use a telecare product or service
>
> **Fact:** That's one in ten people over 65 years of age
>
> **Fact:** That's not very many

Take a look at telecare

Once upon a time, the only technology available to help make older people's lives safer in the home were pendant alarms or panic buttons. These are still in use today, but they now come in greater varieties and are only the tip of the telecare product iceberg.

Also, once upon a time, the availability of products was largely dependent on where you lived. But with the expansion of the industry as a whole over the past twenty years, service providers often now operate on a nationwide basis and pretty much offer a complete range of products.

And finally once upon a time... as the industry was in its infancy and was operating in the new technology space, it had a reputation of letting some people down. People would spend a lot of money installing high tech telecare systems, only to have the supplier go bust and close down after a short time. Whilst this is still a small risk associated with the relative newness of the industry, there is now:

- A considerable number of large, established, reputable service providers, who have a proven track record and can (hopefully!) be relied upon to be around for many years to come.

- A move towards shared, plug-and-play technology, much like the rest of the computer industry with standard USB connections and IT hardware and application connectivity. This means that if a service provider does go bust, the equipment you have paid for can continue to be supported by an alternate supplier.

- A better regulatory and self-governing framework, where telecare businesses are encouraged to support one another in the development of the industry as a whole, via trade associations and representative bodies.

Running through the variety of telecare products, the critical thing to remember is that:

Prevention is better than cure.

Remember: Just because your ageing loved one is perfectly fit right now and has never had a fall or emergency in the home, doesn't mean that they never will. Statistics show that every day in the UK, people do!

Also: Is it not better to have an alarm and not need it, than to not have an alarm and need it?

People don't need to get a thousand products and turn their loved one's house into something that resembles the NASA launch control room.

However, if they don't even take a little time to find out about telecare alternatives and check out what might be helpful, then they may be doing themselves and their future wellbeing a disservice.

Also, depending on circumstances and eligibility, funding for telecare products may be available from your loved one's healthcare provider or various charities and organisations.

Carer Min

I have encountered many people who insist on leaving their alarm beside the bed, on the kitchen table or in their walker basket. They believe that if they need assistance, they'll be able to get to it in an emergency.

Older people are just the same as the rest of us, in that we all tend to believe that we are invincible. That is, until a serious accident occurs.

Again, it is best if a person's carers can actively and regularly encourage that these neck/wrist alarms be worn at all times.

There are lots of different telecare products available in the UK today. And with all of the advances in technology, smart phones, laptops, applications and the digital this-and-thats, the choice is growing every year. A few of the products are:

Falls detectors for the day and night:

- identifying falls and automatically raising alarm
- alerting or waking narcolepsy sufferers

Bed epilepsy sensor:

- identifying an epileptic fit and sending an alert

Enuresis sensor:

- early warning sensor in the bed for incontinence sufferers

Pendant or wrist alarm:

- providing confidence and sense of safety for a vulnerable person to go outdoors and maintain their social engagements
- providing confidence and sense of safety for older people to go about their daily living in and around their home

Radio pull cords, sounder beacons and carer pagers:

- helping those with communication difficulties
- raising an alarm for help

Message prompters as reminders for:

- medication
- locked doors and windows
- turning off appliances like ovens or heaters
- preparing and eating meals
- calling loved ones to confirm they are safe and well

Smoke, gas and flood alarms for:

- raising an alarm day or night, when your loved one's house needs to be evacuated

Chair and bed occupancy sensors and movement and exit door sensors for:

- enabling people with dementia to live independent lives.
- allowing concerned people the chance to unobtrusively monitor their ageing loved one's movements or lack thereof and receive notification if they unexpectedly leave their home

Panic buttons and door and window alarms:

- allowing people to raise an alarm should they be fearful of an intruder or bogus caller

And last, but not least... From a carer's perspective...

Telecare products provide carers with an increased opportunity to relax and take some time out.

If people can apply some technology to help, then why not?

And... help make their loved one's life safer, healthier and happier too!

For further detailed information about all telecare products that are available, potential funding options and leading telecare product and service providers, please visit the Resources page on our website: **www.ActionForAgeing.com/resources**

ACTION STEPS – Telecare Products

1. Gather information about what telecare products are available and how much they cost. ☐

2. Sit down with your loved one and discuss the products. ☐

3. Consider not just what is valid or required for now, but also what might be useful in the future. ☐

4. Discuss telecare products with your loved one's GP to find out what might be suitable. ☐

5. Assess telecare options and potential telecare providers. Products and services can vary from the basic to the highly customised. All are designed to improve your ageing loved one's safety, health and happiness. ☐

6. Remind people that it's better to have an alarm and not use it, than not have an alarm and need it. ☐

Vision safety

> **Fact:** There are twice as many people afraid of going blind as there are afraid of heart disease or premature death
>
> **Fact:** Having an eye test at least every two years can significantly help prevent many forms of eye disease from progressing to a serious extent

Our sight is one of our most precious assets so it makes sense that people do all they can to help maintain the health of their eyes. Unfortunately, as with many of the potential ailments and challenges of ageing, we are not as vigilant about prevention or treatment as we could be.

What can be done to keep eyes healthy?

The most important action people can encourage their ageing loved ones to do is have their eyes tested regularly (at least every 2 years) by an optometrist, even if they are not having any problems with their vision. In fact, up to 40% of someone's optic nerve can be damaged before any noticeable loss of vision occurs, so waiting for a 'sure sign' of vision deterioration is definitely not a good idea.

Also, with eye disease like glaucoma, the deterioration can be very gradual whilst one of the most important factors for successful treatment is early detection! So the key message here is to encourage your ageing loved ones to get their eyes checked regularly.

It is also useful to remind people that exposure to sunlight (even the UK sun, not just the blazing desert and tropical variety!) can contribute to eyesight deterioration. This is because it is the ultraviolet light that can lead to cornea and cataract damage and possibly contribute to macular degeneration (refer below for definition).

Some studies have indicated that eating particular foods might be useful in promoting eye health. The old theory about eating carrots is still open for debate, but there is evidence that vitamins of the A-C-E complex and zinc can help reduce the growth of existing and low-grade age-related macular deterioration. Eating fruits and vegetables and lightly cooking the vegetables as opposed to eating them raw or overcooking them is believed to be the best way to release the nutrients.

By encouraging our ageing loved ones to eat healthily, we can also help them to reduce the likelihood of diabetes. This is important because, among other things, type-2 diabetes (non-insulin diabetes that effects 90% of people with diabetes) is the leading cause of blindness in adults. Diabetes is shown to not only increase the likelihood of glaucoma and cataracts but for 45% of people with diabetes, results in diabetic retinopathy.

In a nutshell, for encouraging healthy eyesight you might suggest:

- a regular eye test with a specialist, at least every 2 years
- safety glasses where appropriate at work or for DIY around the house
- having a balanced diet and eating the recommended 5 portions of fruit and vegetables a day will provide the nutrients for good overall health and promote eye health at the same time!
- lightly cooking vegetables as opposed to eating them raw or overcooking, for maximum nutrients

- safety glasses during sports or activities where eye injuries are common (e.g. playing squash)
- wearing sunglasses (that have the CE mark to show they comply with European safety standards)
- quit smoking as not only does it cause bad breath, but it has been linked to macular degeneration as well as cataract and optic nerve damage
- reduce prolonged periods of staring at a computer screen as it can lead to CVS (computer vision syndrome – that can cause headaches, eyestrain, blurry vision and other focal issues)
- check family history to see if glaucoma is prevalent, as it can be hereditary and can even sometimes skip generations!
- find out about first aid for eye injuries so that if anything happens, there is a better chance of helping the situation rather than doing something to make things worse

What can happen to people's vision?

There are many types of eye condition that can lead to sight impairment or blindness.

Four common types of eye condition for older people are –

Age-related macular degeneration (AMD): This is where the vision in the centre of the eye is gradually lost, resulting in a black spot in the person's sight. If a big white canvas is your eye, it is like someone has walked up and sprayed black paint right into the middle of the canvas. The symptoms can be the black spot described above or blurred or distorted vision, a sensitivity to light or having difficulty in recognising people's faces. Unfortunately, the vast majority of AMD cases are untreatable.

Cataracts: This is where people's vision becomes cloudy or blurred and if cataracts are caught at an early stage, the condition is generally treatable. This is one of the main reasons people (older people especially) should certainly have a regular eye check-up (at least every two years). The cause of cataracts is not exactly known, but it is easy to diagnose and the condition can be treated with a relatively simple operation (often in one day).

Diabetic retinopathy: Diabetes is a common condition where a person's body is not producing enough insulin to break down the components of glucose, which in turn means the body is not generating its fuel efficiently. With diabetic retinopathy, it is the retina and the blood vessels in the eye that are damaged, causing black spots across a person's central vision. For people with diabetes, the best protection against sight-threatening retinopathy is a regular, annual eyesight check-up. The earlier the condition is detected, the earlier it can be halted and managed thereafter with treatment such as laser surgery. The treatment will not be able to repair the damage, but it should help prevent it getting any worse. Hence, the importance of eye tests and early detection! Whilst it is likely that people will retain their peripheral vision, they may still experience significant central vision impairment.

Glaucoma: Glaucoma is a term that captures a number of conditions related to damage to the optic nerve. The condition can be acute, happening very quickly due to an eye fluid blockage or chronic, developing slowly over time where the person's field of vision gradually and painlessly reduces. The field of vision reduces until such a point that only a small, central vision area is operating. This advanced stage of glaucoma is referred to as Tunnel Vision. If acute glaucoma is experienced, there can be a sudden and very painful pressure behind the eye. However, as it will usually evolve slowly, glaucoma is not often detectable by the person with it, until it is at an advanced stage. The causes of glaucoma can be diabetes, age, family history, race and where short-sightedness is already being experienced. Chronic glaucoma is however, quite easily detected and treatment (for example, eye drops or laser surgery) can mean that the condition will not get any worse. Again, this is why encouraging you ageing loved ones (and yourself) to have a regular eye test is so very important.

So THE DOCTOR SAID I SHOULD GET AN EYE TEST. WELL, I BET YOU KNOW WHAT I TOLD HIM!

In between periodic eye tests, where there is concern about the deterioration of someone's eyesight, it is important to seek the advice of a GP or eye specialist.

For the person concerned and their loved ones, this can be a very difficult, stressful and anxious time. The issue of potential sight loss or blindness requires great sensitivity and quite often the person with the condition or the people close to them may need to receive assistance such as counselling or advice on potential outcomes and ways in which to maintain wellbeing.

There are a large variety of assistive technologies and products and services available to help people with sight loss maintain and improve their wellbeing. Amongst other uses, these items and services can help maintain independence by enhancing people's methods of communication, providing them with entertainment and promoting their home safety.

The list of available technologies includes screen magnifiers, text-to-speech software (that converts text to audio), Braille technology, large monitors, audio players, speech recognition software, digital books, alternative keyboards, remote controls and telephones with extra large buttons,

Products to help with independence and safety around the home include such items as bread slices (with guard), cups that make a noise when they are nearly full, large font books, audio books, talking watches and the list goes on for some time and then a bit more.

Services such as counselling, housing advice, funding advice and the signposting of local activity groups and service providers can be accessed via charities and other organisations.

Before deciding on any products and services for your ageing loved ones, a useful process to follow is to gather as much information as possible about the different options and then contact their GP or an organisation such as a charity, who can offer reliable, independent advice.

For information about sight loss and the support and counselling services available to those who are impacted directly or indirectly, the best places to start are the UK's major sight-related charities such as the Royal National Institute of Blind People (RNIB) **www.rnib.org.uk** and Action for Blind People: **www.ActionForBlindPeople.org.uk**

Both can also be contacted through the RNIB Helpline: **0303 123 9999**

If you wish to find out more information about sight impairment, reputable organisations and the products and services available, please visit the resources page on our website: **www.ActionForAgeing.com/resources**

Volunteering

> **Fact:** 27% of people over 65 are involved in volunteering.

Volunteering is where people give their time and effort for free to something that is intended to improve the wellbeing of others (other than or including their family). Some people are actively involved in volunteer work all through their life whilst others become more interested or find the time when they are older and may have fewer competing commitments. Whatever the time of people's life

So, MISTER SURANA, WHEN DID YOU RETIRE FROM WORKING AT THE TOWER OF LONDON?

Charity Shop

that they choose to start, the common experience shared by volunteers is that a great many benefits are to be gained and enjoyed by helping improve the wellbeing of others. In short, it's good to give.

What people choose to give, depends entirely on them. 'Giving' for some is selling all their earthly possessions, handing the money to a local Lost Dogs Home and spending their days sorting bags of recycled rubbish in exchange for somewhere to pitch their tent. For others, 'giving' is belonging to a befriending service and calling a lonely older person once a week for a 30 minute chat. Whilst for others, 'giving' is spending three months arranging a charity auction at a grand hotel and gently encouraging millionaires to write big cheques for great causes. Whilst for others again, 'giving' is spending four hours every Monday morning at their local charity shop helping to dress the front window or hoping on a plane to Ghana and heading to a small village to teach children to read. Whether it is big, small, global, local, public or private, these are all very worthy ways to volunteer and all can be very rewarding for those giving and those receiving.

It's good to give

People of all ages can and do perform voluntary work in all sorts of ways. A short list of ideas on different forms of volunteering is provided later. The benefits people get out of it are varied and depend very much on the volunteer's individual circumstances. For older people such as your ageing loved ones, the potential benefits of volunteering can be that it:

- Provides a sense of purpose. For people who are in between jobs or aren't working, being a volunteer can provide a great deal of satisfaction that they are needed and doing something useful with their time and energy.

- Provides social interaction. For older people who are not working or actively involved in local social activities, isolation or loneliness can be a problem. By volunteering, people can enjoy the opportunity of interaction with the public and with other volunteers.

- Being welcomed by and working as part of a team is a great way to build self esteem and confidence.

- Older people get to put to good use their knowledge, experiences and skills (human capital). They might know all about gardening and be able to help someone with mobility issues to transform their garden into containing only low maintenance plants. Or they might be able to show a young apprentice window cleaner how to get up and down a wet ladder without killing themselves.

- They get the opportunity to learn new skills and develop knowledge about completely new subjects. They may have worked in an office all their life and are now able to volunteer with the local song group as the social activities coordinator.

- They get to meet a wider variety of people than they have ever come in contact with and develop new, positive relationships. If someone has been a plumber in Bristol their whole life and volunteer for a one year placement in Peru to help build water wells and irrigation systems for crops, it's a fair bet they will met some different types of people in their travels.

- If someone has lost a loved one such as a partner, volunteering can help keep them busy and take their mind off their loss. It can also help by providing them with satisfaction of helping others and providing comfort to people less fortunate than they are, as well as provide new social interaction to help avoid the social isolation that losing a partner can sometimes result in.

- They get to develop new life skills and communication methods because they are learning how to do new activities and interacting with a greater variety of people than they usually might do.

- The hours for volunteering are very flexible and can be done part time or full time. If part time, people can commit from a few minutes a day up to a few days per week. People who volunteer for a telephone befriending service may only make a call to a person once a week for 30 minutes whilst a person manning the reception desk of an older people's shelter might be in there 10am – 6pm, Monday-Wednesday.

- Volunteers often experience a tremendous boost to their self-esteem as a result of helping others and performing an activity for the public good.

- Working in a positive and caring environment with other volunteers who are also sharing the benefits of the experience can be very good for people's mental attitude and wellbeing. There is a great camaraderie amongst volunteers, whether they are handing out pamphlets, collecting data for a survey or clearing a riverbank of litter.

- Volunteering is a great way to stay active and help promote a person's mental and physical wellbeing. Whether people are helping to sort donated goods in a charity store room and price the items or they are outside working in a team planting trees, they will be giving their brains and bodies a good workout.

These are just a few of the benefits a loved one can experience if they decide to volunteer.

In short, it's good to give!

What is also helpful to remind your ageing loved ones is that they have a great deal to offer by volunteering and that organisations really do appreciate and value the particular contribution that older people can provide.

Some of the reasons organisations are keen to have older volunteers are because:

- They have often developed a broader range of communication skills and, because of their extra years of experience, they are more likely to understand, empathise with and relate to a wider range of people than younger people may be able to. For roles such as bereavement counselling, some people may feel more comfortable talking with an older person who may have had a similar experience.

- They possess skill sets and knowledge that have been accumulated over many years of experience. There are many things that can be learnt from books and there are many things that can only be learnt from trial and error. A school teacher who has been dealing with teenage students for 40 years will certainly have a few tricks up their sleeve that aren't covered in the Teacher Training Manual.

- Where budgets are tight in most volunteer organisations, older people may be able to offer simple, practical and cheap solutions to problems. If a power generator breaks down, rather than waiting for a new spare part to be delivered, they may have temporary fix that keeps it running in the meantime.

- They can have greater maturity and common sense that can help in being able to handle challenging situations that can crop up. A person may be a volunteer helping people with dementia and one of the people they are caring for becomes distressed. As an older person, the volunteer may be better equipped to help settle the agitated person and resolve things in a safe and sensitive manner.

- Older volunteers often display a tremendous amount of loyalty, patience and tolerance in their activities that has come from their sense of commitment and a lifetime of experience.

- They can also require minimal training and supervision because they bring a great many skills and a seasoned sense of responsibility with them.

- Older volunteers can often also be more flexible with time, as they may have fewer commitments than people with young families and jobs.

When discussing volunteering with your loved ones, it might also be helpful to have a list of examples of the sorts of things people can do. Some people may dismiss the idea of volunteering as they think it's 'only' working at the local charity shop, or helping an older person to do their shopping. In reality, there are an infinite number and variety of actions that volunteers can perform, depending on their skills, preferences, time and energy.

A short list of volunteering activities to get the conversation rolling are:

- Activity leader or assistant, being involved in the organisation and running of activities such as a song group, knitting group, gallery visits, book club, art and craft activities, swimming club, excursions locally or even trips abroad.

- Befriending, by visiting someone regularly in their home or calling them on the telephone each week for a chat, helping them to feel less isolated and giving them someone to talk to.

- Home handyperson help, doing jobs around a person's home such as changing light bulbs, putting up pictures, painting the bathroom, removing unwanted furniture, moving a bed to a better position, installing a grab rail or shower chair in the bathroom or a smoke alarm in the hallway.

- Becoming a deckhand on a deep sea fishing boat during Winter, off the coast of Alaska. Okay, that is more to see if people are paying attention when you are reading them the list of ideas.
- Community volunteering, working on projects in their local area to improve the environment and wellbeing of their neighbours.
- Activity Buddy, helping people become involved or maintain involvement in an activity such as a stroll through a nearby heath, going to a weekly foreign language class, attending a singing group or dancing class, a walk to the shops for the weekly essentials, attending sports matches, tai-chi classes or participating in neighbourhood fundraising or awareness raising activities.
- Bereavement and loss visitor. A very special and important role that older people are especially suited to and needed for.
- In a local charity shop dressing the windows, helping with admin, serving at the counter, driving the van to pick up goods, contacting manufacturers to ask about donating returns, discontinued or excess stock, in the stock room managing stock volumes and distribution, sorting bric-a-brac, pricing items, preparing goods for sale, helping prepare leaflets and performing marketing activities, dressing the in-store presentations and providing training and exchanging knowledge with new staff members.
- High wire trapeze artist in a travelling circus. Can disregard. Another attention-tester!
- Events assistant, such as providing information at charity fun runs, handing out name badges at a charity auction or pamphlets at a Falls Awareness event.
- Helper at a Day Centre, co-ordinating or assisting in activities, providing decorations, helping residents with daily tasks, providing manicures or playing cards.

- Being a driver, transporting people to appointments, events and activities or helping pick up and deliver items for a charity or local organisation.

- Being a fundraiser, rallying awareness, asking for involvement and donations from people and businesses and holding large or small fundraising events from charity auctions and sponsored walks to a dinner for six and gathering up all the loose coins that family and friends have around their home.

- For green thumbs or those who want to learn, being a volunteer Gardener can be very rewarding, helping people in their home to maintain their garden or develop a new one that is more suitable for them to manage as their strength, agility and mobility may be decreasing over the years to come.

- Being a fund raiser by doing rope-free, high speed rock climbing straight up the 13,000ft North Face of the Eiger. The record is around two and a half hours. Before suggesting this to your ageing loved one, perhaps they should read the Falls Awareness Topic in this book first.

- Working with information and advice, maybe on a telephone helpline or on the counter at a local information booth.

- Volunteering as an IT coach, helping people with queries, providing training on how to get on and use the internet, how to print documents, or perform online shopping for groceries, books and everything else under the sun.

- Being a swimming monitor at the local pool, assisting in swimming classes and arranging games or water sports such as water volleyball or water aerobics.

- People can volunteer to be a trustee for a charity. Trustees are people who are legally responsible for the management and decision-making of a charity. It is a very important position with legal and financial responsibilities and obligations, so people who are interested in such a role need to be thoroughly aware of what it entails.

- Charity administration, helping with the day-to-day admin of running a charity, with activities like collecting and inputting survey information and data processing of the charity activities, helping train staff, working in communications, IT, management, strategy and in creative and marketing roles such as graphic design and copywriting for the charity publications and content for their website and contacting sponsors and speakers for events.

- Volunteering to work abroad in disadvantaged villages or towns can be very rewarding. They have roles for people of all ages and a variety of experience and backgrounds, for terms that usually range from three months up to two years. It doesn't suit everyone but for those who are interested, there are a huge variety of roles that

are offered by organisations who specialise in placing foreign volunteers in some of the world's most desperate locations. Roles include teachers (all levels, ages and subjects), small business advisors, tradespeople such as plumbers, electricians and builders, advocacy specialists, agriculture advisors, natural resource advisors (e.g. water, forestry, fisheries and coastal), project managers, small business advisors, social workers, vocational trainers, IT trainers, tourism and marketing managers, fundraisers, nurses, doctors, occupational thera-pists, community workers, engineers, urban planners, drivers and... the list goes on.

- Being the Chief Test Dummy at a company that makes bullet-proof vests. Only kidding. But people are welcome to give it a shot. So to speak...

If your ageing loved ones have not been actively involved in volunteering before, they may not be aware of the huge variety of very interesting and rewarding roles that can be considered (or a few of those that shouldn't be).

Plus, volunteering can be very flexible, as people can commit to as much or as little time or effort as they wish.

Volunteering isn't for everyone and that is absolutely fine. But, if people are at least aware of what is on offer and what the benefits to themselves and others can be, then who knows what might happen!

If you or your loved ones wish to find out more about volunteering opportunities and organisations that can help find them a suitable role locally (or abroad) that they would enjoy, please visit the Resources page on our website: **www.ActionForAgeing.com/Resources**

ACTION STEPS – Volunteering

1. Enquire if your loved ones are interested in volunteering. ☐

2. If not, maybe share with them the list of benefits that people can enjoy and all of the reasons why charities and organisations really appreciate what older people can bring to the roles. ☐

3. It is certainly worth reminding people that there is a huge variety of volunteering roles available. The list we have included is just the tip of the iceberg. ☐

4. Plus, volunteering can be very flexible! ☐

TOPIC 52

Walkers & mobility aids

Fact: 70% of over 65s in the UK who need mobility help rely on just a walking stick.

Fact: that translates to 3.3 million people whose mobility may be seriously impacted because of an inappropriate walking aid.

Mobility aids are a priority

They're great inventions!

Known as walkers, walking frames or zimmers, they are metal and plastic frames that provide assistance to people for walking. And banging into teenagers who get in their way.

Walkers have meant that many people (400,000 in the UK) are able to move around their homes, gardens, restaurants and shopping centres, with relative ease.

Where once they would have been housebound or had to rely upon a walking stick for support, the introduction of the walker means their weight is spread across the four corners of the walking frame, thus giving them the gift of mobility and hence independence.

- Unfortunately, in the UK, 70% of older people needing help with mobility still have to rely on a standard walking stick. That translates to 3.3 million citizens.

This is because nearly half of all mobility aids are provided by the government and public funds are already stretched.

So people who require a walking frame, or something other than a walking stick, may be unable to receive one or experience a long delay until they do.

The five million people who purchase their own mobility aids when they need them, are therefore more likely to select a product that suits their needs, rather than what the local health service provider's budget allows for.

Where your loved one appears to be on the cusp of having mobility issues, be it through deteriorating vision and balance or a general increase in tripping frequency, then early action on using a mobility aid is critical.

> If concerns about mobility have been raised, why wait until your loved one has an accident before getting them a product?

Walking sticks, crutches, trollies, wheelchairs and scooters are all great alternatives to assist people in getting around.

And it's likely your loved one will need help with mobility, given:

- 25% of 70-80 year-olds need permanent mobility assistance
- with the over-85s, more than 50% have permanently impaired mobility

And what can be very helpful for people is their walker.

Walkers come in all sorts of varieties with multiple functions:

- some are designed to help people up from a seated position into their walker (hi-riser style)
- trays built in for eating meals from or adjustable arm pads that people can rest their weight on

- non-slip handlebars
- extra large and durable wheels
- a built-in seat
- can be folded up into a carrier bag
- multiple basket and storage configurations

The options are enormous.

So if your loved one is experiencing any mobility issues at all, it is definitely worth seeking the advice of a healthcare professional about:

- Is a mobility aid required?
- If so, what mobility aid is most suitable?

One additional tip – don't let your ageing loved one use their shopping trolley as a walker, as it is not sturdy enough and is more likely to cause a fall by flipping over and sending your loved one flying!

A variety of walker known as a rollator is a heavy duty version of a walker, but with four wheels instead of two.

Carer Min

A word of caution. One client I had become very tired on me in the shopping centre. In other words, his legs gave way and he suggested that he sit on the seat of the rollator whilst I pushed him back to the car.

I reluctantly had to refuse his request because it was quite a lumpy path and if he had slipped off the seat he would have injured himself.

Instead, we rested until he was able to safely make the walk back.

Health and Safety regulations may sometimes seem extreme, but the fact is that professional carers and the people they are looking after need to have clear instructions on what should and shouldn't be done.

Where agreed procedures and processes aren't followed, people's safety is potentially more at risk.

When people are caring for their own loved ones they should very carefully consider following Health and Safety recommendations before deciding on a course of action.

Carer Min

A little suggestion is that whilst the person is sitting in a comfortable seat they be given a damp cloth to use to wipe down their walker in order to avoid a coating of dust and grime building up.

If you would like to find out more information about walkers and other mobility aids, please visit the Resources page on our website: **www.ActionForAgeing.com/Resources**

ACTION STEPS – Walker/mobility aids

1. Monitor your loved one's mobility. ☐

2. If they start to have any mobility issues, seek medical advice. ☐

3. It is better to obtain and use a walker or mobility aid before they have an accident, not just after (as is usually the case). ☐

Wish list

A very unfortunate result of some conditions (such as dementia) or injuries is that people may lose some or all of their ability to communicate.

The list below is something that people of all ages should spend five minutes completing. If anything ever did happen, at least then their loved ones will be in a better position to help with their wellbeing.

It is the sort of list that most people don't ever think about needing or will likely ever need.

However, accidents do happen and as it takes only five minutes to fill in and is free to write up, it is worth doing and putting in the 'Hopefully Will Never Need' folder.

A simple action that can impact years of wellbeing.

If you wish to print out or download a full scale version, please visit the Resources page on our website: **www.ActionForAgeing.com**

It's okay – no need to report a theft – the list is over the page!

Wellbeing action list

In the event that I can't tell you these things myself, please keep the following in mind.

Name:_____

My favourite:

Colours:_____

Music: _____

_____

Foods:_____

_____

_____

Drink: _____

Books: _____

TV shows: _____

_____

Films:_____

_____

Views:_____

_____

Day trips: _____

Dream destination: _____

Working

> *"I'd rather wear out than rust"*
>
> ## *Carer Min*

Just because our loved ones are at or near the State retirement age does not mean that they necessarily have any plan or wish to retire. In the UK the mandatory retirement age has been removed, the state pension age has been increased and the baby boomer generation has just started to reach sixty-five years old. So the proportion of older people in the workforce is looking to increase year-on-year for some time to come.

The value and positive contribution that older workers bring to the work environment are well documented and widely appreciated. That said, it is important to continue to remind people of this, so that older workers can feel confident and enthusiastic about the opportunities ahead of them and that society can continue to recognise, use and encourage the continuing contribution of older workers into their seventies, eighties, or even nineties.

There are also government schemes, charities and organisations that are set up to help unemployed older people find work or start a new business of their own, with the provision of funding, training, support and mentoring. Other schemes and projects have been set up for worker solutions such as job-sharing, where two employees who wish to work part time share the role and responsibilities of one full time worker.

This is all good news for your ageing loved ones, as the focus on trying to remove age discrimination from the workplace and raise the profile of the 'ageism in the workplace' debate, means that people are at least trying to make an effort to provide for the wellbeing of older workers. This isn't to say that we are on the cusp of a working environment Utopia where no discrimination exists, no negative stereotypes appear and everyone is judged purely on their own merits. That would be nice and that is the goal of course. But we aren't there just yet.

Work options:

The work options that are available to your ageing loved one are the same as everyone else. They can be in or looking for full time or part time employment in the private or public sectors, or interested in working for an NGO (non-governmental organisation), charity or social enterprise in what is referred to as the third sector (or civil society).

Whilst the potential work sectors might be similar between the different generations, the reasons your ageing loved one now has for wanting to work may be different from earlier in their career. This is to be expected, as the benefits of work change as people's needs change over time. And the needs of a thirty year old are quite different from a seventy year old.

If your ageing loved one passes the state pension age and is deciding whether or not they wish (or perhaps need) to keep working, some of the recognised benefits are:

- they may feel happy and secure in their current job
- they may try working in a new industry that has always been of interest but never had quite the right position for them
- keep earning money rather than receiving a pension
- remain active and maintain a good life/work balance
- utilise their human capital (knowledge, competencies and characteristics)
- help and train younger workers
- to maintain, enjoy and develop social interaction and activity
- to provide structure and time management in their day. After a lifetime of working and delivering to bosses, clients or customers, the position of being retired and not having to do anything during their day can be more than a little odd for some people
- increasing availability of more flexible work hours or job sharing. Part time hours can mean 20-30 hours per week or even 5-15 hours too. Lovely if that suits!

Some people may mistakenly feel that employers may hold negative views about the value and contribution of their older workers. However, studies from around the world have consistently shown that employers and businesses value their older workers very highly. Reasons for this include:

- have greater reliability, motivation and loyalty than the younger workers
- better skills, knowledge and experience

- more dedicated, flexible and punctual
- have better communication and organisational skills
- less absenteeism
- greater empathy and customer relations
- better capacity for mentoring
- less likely to suffer workplace accidents
- their experience enables them apply for jobs that are more appropriate to their skill set, therefore resulting in improved performance and less job-hopping

An alternative that is appealing to increasing numbers of people who are over 60, is to start their own business. The motivation might be because a fantastic opportunity has been identified, a new product dreamt up or they simply have a desire to see how they go turning their hand to something entrepreneurial. They might have a hobby or interest that they can turn into a small business building model railway bridges from toilet rolls or a very large business building a new car that can run on orange juice. They may have limited opportunity for employment where they are living or with their skill set, so they decide to start their own business instead. They may want to start a charity or enterprise to perform good works or to build as a legacy to hand onto their family or community. They might have oodles of cash and be bored ridgid or they might be stone broke and scared ridgid. Whatever their motivation is to start a new business, there are charities, organisations, businesses and government schemes that have been set up to help, by providing resources such as funding, mentoring, support, equipment, training and access to extensive networks.

For your ageing loved one, whether they are looking for full time or part time work or starting their own business, the key is that they receive emotional support from their friends and family. If people are struggling to find work it can have a very heavy impact on their confidence and self-esteem. It is critical therefore, that the people who know and love them the most are aware of and sensitive to the potentially tough time their loved one is having and to try and offer them as much support and encouragement and as many ideas (where appropriate) as possible.

Some things people can do to help their loved ones who may be struggling to find work are:

- Talk about it with them. Help to reduce any potential sense of shame by discussing things in a sensitive way and reassuring them that their friends and family understand. Reminding them how successful their brother or sister is, probably isn't such a good idea.
- Let them know that they are not a burden or seen as a burden.
- Take the initiative and contact them, on the phone or meet up with them in person and chat about their job seeking over a beer or cup of tea.
- Try to help them maintain realistic expectations so as to focus on achievable roles and avoid unnecessary, predictable disappointments.
- Try to be supportive but not pushy.
- Avoid blaming them for their own situation (even if that may be

the case). Such negativity won't help them get a job and it may put up more barriers to communication.

- Avoid nagging. Being on someone's case and abusing them for not trying is not an effective way to get them to take action.

- Encouraging your loved one and praising every positive step they make will help make them feel better about themselves and help them one step closer to getting a job.

- Let them know that it is okay to have bad days occasionally.

- Try to balance out validation and finding a solution. Along the lines of "It's okay, you aren't the only one who is having a difficult time. Especially with the local economy as it is. Maybe if I give you some help identifying some businesses to approach?"

- Help them keep their problems in perspective. Maybe remind them that you or someone you both know has been in the situation before or that they have many things going well in their life (family, experiences) that they can enjoy and feel grateful for and that their current struggle will one day be over. Very few people are faced with absolutely never being able to find work in some capacity, ever again.

When people are heading towards, through or have past the State pension age and aren't interested in full time retirement, then there are many wonderful options and opportunities available. Whilst some are keen on staying in the private or public sectors, many other people also look to providing their energies and skills in the voluntary sector on a part time or full time basis. For more information on the benefits and opportunities of volunteering, please refer to our topic 'Volunteering' on page 321 of this book.

AGE Platform Europe

In the Resources section, you can also find links to the AGE Platform Europe. The AGE Platform is a European network of organisations of and for people who are fifty plus, which aims to provide a voice and promote the interests of senior citizens across Europe. The Platform has seven main policy areas: Anti-discrimination, Employment and Active Ageing, Social Inclusion, Social Protection, Health, Accessibility and Solidarity between Generations.

The AGE Platform creates and collects a huge wealth of information about employment for the over-fifties. **www.age-platform.org**

For more information on charities, organisations and government schemes that are focused on helping older people find suitable work, be it part time or full time, paid or voluntary, at home or abroad, then please visit the Resources section of our website: **www.ActionForAgeing.com**

Wise Owls is a service that offers employment support to older (50-65+) working age people who are looking for work or self employment. As the first UK specialist older working age support organisation and website they can offer everyone in the UK online and phone support – phone their Promoting Age Diversity hotline on **020 7278 5191** or email **pad@wiseowls.co.uk**. Wise Owls can also provide one-to-one support to over-50s living in London.

On the Wise Owls website, you can gain access to hundreds of job vacancies each week, plus a range of training and allied expert support through their websites **www.wiseowls.co.uk** and **www.equalityrecruitment.co.uk** – which between them receive nearly 1 million hits per month.

ACTION STEPS – Working

1. Ensure your ageing loved one knows that their contribution to the workforce is appreciated. ☐

2. Work is available on a full time or part time basis, paid and voluntary, from as few as five hours per week. ☐

3. There are local community programs and national government, charity and organisation schemes that are focused on helping your ageing loved one find a job that is satisfying. ☐

4. There are many fantastic reasons why people may wish to continue working after they have reached the state pension age. A whole list above – to name but a few! ☐

5. Employers know what a great job older workers do and what value they add to the workplace. ☐

6. People of all ages can start their own business. There are many associations and schemes out there to help businesses get launched. ☐

7. Where a loved one may be struggling with being unemployed or the fear of losing their job and not being able to find another one, that is where they will rely most on their friends and family for love, encouragement and support. ☐

8. There are many wonderful opportunities for older people to work and find personal satisfaction and fulfilment in a wide variety of industry sectors. The more that people can do to help build a bridge between their loved one's hopes and aspirations and the reality and richness of their daily life, the greater their sense of wellbeing can be. ☐

Cancer – it can pop up anywhere!

> **Fact:** 1 in 3 people in UK will develop cancer during their lifetime
>
> **Fact:** Of those with cancer, 1 in 4 will die from it
>
> **Fact:** Sixty five per cent of cancer cases occur in those aged 65 and over
>
> **Fact:** Breast, prostate, lung and colorectum cancers account for over half of all cases in people over 65 years of age

What is cancer?

Cancer is where cells in the body are abnormal and their growth is uncontrolled. These cancerous cells are also referred to as malignant cells.

What types are common in older people

Cancer can start in tissue anywhere in the body and there are approximately 200 different types that have been identified.

For people over 65 years old, the most common cancers are breast, prostate, lung, colorectum, uterus, bladder and ovary.

Early detection of cancer is one of the best ways to successfully treat it.

Early detection relies upon people:
– being aware of the warning signs
– taking action when a warning sign is first noticed

What are the risk factors

Age – As the process of cells becoming cancerous often takes a long time to develop, the incidence of cancer becomes higher as we age.

Genetics – Some people have a genetic predisposition towards cancer, because they already have a gene fault when they are born or perhaps they have inherited characteristics that make them more susceptible to a particular kind of cancer. For example, people with fair skin, many moles and a close relative who has had melanoma are at a higher risk than average of experiencing skin cancer.

Immune system – Those whose immune systems have experienced difficulties are more likely to get virus-sourced cancer, such as cervical cancer or types such as lymphomas.

Bodyweight – After tobacco, obesity is the most known avoidable cause of cancer with particular increased risk of pancreatic and bowel cancer and breast cancer in women post-menopause.

Diet – Linked to body weight and obesity, research indicates that an unhealthy diet can lead to an increased risk of cancer. A high intake of red meat, processed meat, salt and saturated fat can increase risk of cancer whilst a diet that is high in fibre, fruit and vegetables can help lower the incidence of cancer.

Physical Activity – People have a higher risk of cancer if they are less physically active.

Environment – If people are regularly exposed to tobacco smoke, work place hazards, radiation, material such as asbestos or even prolonged time spent in the sun, they are at an increased risk of developing cancer.

Carer Min

EARLY DETECTION IS VERY IMPORTANT!!

What are the symptoms?

- Moles on your skin changing
- Feeling fatigue frequently
- Changes in skin colour and feel
- Changes in bowel habit
- Frequent unexplained coughing or hoarseness
- Abnormal bleeding
- Ulcers or sores that never seem to heal
- Feeling a lump on your body
- Having trouble passing urine
- Losing weight unexpectedly
- Experiencing unexplained pain
- Digestion and swallowing difficulty
- Night sweats for no apparent reason

Prevention actions

- **Stop smoking**
- **Limit sun exposure**
- **Healthy diet**
  - balanced diet of fruit and vegetables, moderate red meat
  - reduce meat and animal fat intake (cream, butter, cheese)
  - reduce salt and sugar intake and consumption of fried food
  - reduce alcohol intake
  - increase intake of fibre, cereals, pasta, bread, rice and oily fish (e.g. mackerel, trout and salmon)
  - remember to eat the 5-a-day portions of fruit and vegetables
- **Physical Activity**
  - the overall risk of cancer can be reduced by maintaining regular, moderate physical activity such as a mixture of walking, fast walking and stair walking on a regular (daily) basis
  - a protective effect has been established, for example with physical activity on colon cancer and a reduced risk of breast cancer in women post-menopause

The information we have provided in this topic is not to be taken as medical advice. Please always seek the opinion of a GP or other appropriate healthcare professional for all your and your family's medical matters.

For more information regarding cancer and the various forms of treatment and support that is available, please contact the below leading charities:

Cancer Research UK: **www.cancerresearchuk.org;** for patient information: **www.cancerhelp.org.uk;** Cancer information nurses: UK Freephone: **0808 800 4040** (Monday to Friday 9am-5pm)

Macmillan Cancer Support: **www.macmillan.org.uk**. If you have any questions about cancer, need support or just someone to talk to, please call free, Monday to Friday 9am-8pm (interpretation service available). **(UK) 0808 808 0000**

Additional resources listed in the Resources section of our website: **www.ActionForAgeing.com**

ACTION STEPS – Cancer

1. Help your ageing loved ones to be aware of what the symptoms of cancer can be. ☐

2. Encourage your familiy and friends to take action. ☐

3. Ensure everyone is aware of the importance of taking preventative action. ☐

4. Ensure everyone is aware of the importance of early detection. ☐

5. Ensure people take preventative action, know what some of the common symptoms are and if they have any questions or concerns, to contact their doctor immediately.* ☐

   *If any of the above sounds like it was repeated, that is because it was, in order to ensure that everyone is reminded of the importance of taking preventative steps and early detection in helping to avoid cancer or where possible, reduce its impact!

Closing message from Carer Min

Carer Min – Closing message

Every idea, word written, comment passed and tip suggested in this book has one aim: To assist you to nurture and nourish your ageing loved one during their later years.

We have endeavoured to alert you to the fact that 'falls' are the most common cause of ageing persons losing their independence. I can honestly state that almost every person I have visited over the years has encountered either broken hips or limbs, often having been incurred in the bathroom. Lengthy hospital stays are endured and, more often than not, upon their return home, they have to accept the fact that they can no longer play bowls, take the dog for a walk or drive themselves to the shops.

We all face a difficult challenge to somehow convince our ageing loved ones that they could, in fact, incur a fall at some stage so it really is important to 'use the bath mat'. "Oh, no, it couldn't happen to me because I am very careful". That's what everyone who has ever fallen has thought. With persistent reminders, proactive actions and an ongoing awareness of the possibility of a fall being ever likely, we can significantly help reduce the frequency of falls. That reduction could be for thousands of people in the UK every year. Possibly even millions.

Busy hands are happy hands. How true this saying is when one thinks of our ageing loved ones. I could not nominate the number of older people who have resorted to going for a nap after they've had their cup of tea for breakfast and they'll stay on the bed until it is lunch time. Boredom can be crippling, as can loneliness. Both can be alleviated if there is someone in their life who is prepared to assist them to organise a few activities they can enjoy. Often, once the ageing person is assisted to be organised they are quite happy to be left alone to undertake their activity.

I have encountered so many clients whose friends either can no longer visit because of distance, their own mobility issues, memory issues, or who have, in fact, passed over before them. This can mean their family are the most important factor in their lives. Where possible, getting together for the day, travelling somewhere together or simply sharing a meal, is time well spent. The camaraderie enjoyed around the dining table is one of life's great pleasures. Admittedly, not all families get along. Where this is the case, hopefully a reconciliation of differences will one day take place, or if that is not to be, then hopefully those involved are at least in a position to help implement some of the tips and suggestions in this book to make their life easier and more fulfilling.

Grandchildren are always welcome visitors. To observe these two generations interacting is a special moment. Discussions about tattoos, sex, movies, cars, holidays, are always enlightening. Subjects never discussed with their parents will be openly spoken of with their grandparents. I smile as I remember hearing, long ago, that grandparents and grandchildren have always had one common enemy. The parents. I laughed then, and I laugh now.

You have read the many tips offered in this book. Even by utilising the most simple tip you will make a difference in your ageing loved one's life. Remember, "inch by inch everything's a cinch".

Most of my days begin and end with my offering thanks for the opportunity given to me to help, mix and mingle with older people. These good people have taught me so much. Patience, integrity, tolerance, humour, punctuality, what it was to endure wars, surviving the Depression and the Holocaust and so much more.

I have to tell you that the older people I have had the honour to work with have enriched my life more than I could ever have imagined, and now the next generation of my family is taking up the challenge by devoting their lives to assisting older people and their families too.

One could request no more honourable occupation.

Robin Minett (aka Carer Min)

Index

About the authors

CHRIS MINETT is the founder of Action for Ageing.

The enterprise mission was conceived during a family holiday where stories and challenges from the front line of caring were being shared around the dinner table. Following lengthy discussions where a variety of creative solutions were debated and developed, there was a light bulb moment. Why not keep things simple and promote a commonsense approach to the challenges of later life and care? In short, there needed to be a greater focus on encouraging people to take proactive action for themselves and their ageing loved ones in order to create a safer, healthier and happier later life.

Boiled down, it became 'Prevention is better than cure' and 'Action speaks louder than words'.

Whilst these concepts had been bubbling away over many years during family discussions with an active interest in the various challenges that ageing and care for older people represent to us as individuals and as a society, Chris realised that there was a very real and profound need to help people in our community make a seismic change in their attitude towards ageing and how they can best promote their own and their loved one's wellbeing.

Similar to what occurred from the 1990s until today with regard to the massive change in attitude towards the environment and environmental issues, so too the mindset of society now needs to adjust how it recognises and approaches ageing.

Rather than regarding our ageing population as a burden, it is far better to view it and promote it as an opportunity.

Rather than people ignoring the impact ageing can have on the mind and body, it is better to be aware of the possibilities and then make better-informed lifestyle decisions.

In other words, encouraging people to take proactive action for themselves and their ageing loved ones to create a safer, healthier and happier later life for all.

Hence, Action for Ageing was born.

Originally from Melbourne, Australia, Chris has called London his home for the last 18 years and been self-employed the last 17 years as a business analyst and corporate consultant. He also had a brief and successful stint early on, as a restaurant waiter and a very brief (and not so successful) stint as a restaurant dish washer. He lives with his wife and son.

ROBIN MINETT (Carer Min) has been a 'carer' for as long as she can remember – she just didn't realise it at the time. In her personal life, business life and latest career, the love, respect and personal welfare of others has been a constant companion. A fifteen year trained specialist with older people and dementia care, Robin has worked in every aspect of the industry.

Frontline, personal, day-to-day experience has been gathered in a variety of roles including: carer, team management, activities coordinator, residential care worker, live-in home care, personal care worker and crisis care.

Organisational experience includes working within the frameworks of private homes, community services, local government, charities, various church groups and privately run facilities.

Today Robin finds herself motivated to share her 'caring' stories about the older people she deals with on a daily basis and the various challenges that personal and professional carers face.

Robin is a passionate advocate and spokesperson for older people. When she is not working, writing or rock 'n' roll dancing, Robin can be found dreaming of her next holiday with her grandchildren.

About Action for Ageing

Action for Ageing is a social enterprise committed to improving the wellbeing of older people.

We aim to achieve this by encouraging people to take simple, proactive steps to help promote the health, safety and happiness of their ageing loved ones.

Action for Ageing is working with charities, associations, forums, voluntary and business organisations as well as local, national and international NGOs. We provide engaging and informative content that can be used to get people's attention and motivate them towards taking simple, practical action steps towards a better quality later life. Having raised people's awareness and identified action steps, we then provide the information and sign-posting towards the resources people require to turn those action steps into actions performed.

Action for Ageing activities with organisations include:

- bulk book order fulfilment
- book customisation
- book discount codes
- book affiliate sales opportunities
- speaking engagements for the authors
- book and content syndication
- book and content translations
- book and content licensing

Organisations wishing to discuss any of the above activities or other enterprise opportunities with Action for Ageing can contact us via email: **office@ActionForAgeing.com**

ACTION STEP –
15% discount for family and friends

With our compliments, your friends and family can receive a 15% discount on additional copies of Action For Ageing. They can receive this by entering the discount code **AFA-15** at our website checkout: **www.actionforageing.com/book** For bulk orders of 20 or more copies please contact: **office@ActionForAgeing.com**

Lightning Source UK Ltd.
Milton Keynes UK
UKOW030253231111

182537UK00003B/2/P